"NUMBER, PLEASE!

a history of
the early London telephone exchanges
from 1880 to 1912

The self restoring indicator branching
multiple switchboard at Bank Exchange, 1895

The first telephone exchange in London at 36 Coleman street. A two panel Williams switchboard

"NUMBER, PLEASE!"

a history of
the early London telephone exchanges
from 1880 to 1912

D Occomore

IAN HENRY PUBLICATIONS
PLAYERS PRESS

ISBN 0 86025 462 3

Printed by
Progressive Printing (UK) Ltd.
Unit 5-8 Rutherford Close, Leigh on Sea, Essex SS9 5LQ
for
Ian Henry Publications, Ltd.
20 Park Drive, Romford, Essex RM1 4LH

INTRODUCTION

"Each day the number of users will grow and the more familiar the service becomes the less thought will be given to it." So wrote J E Kingsbury in *The Telephone and Telephone Exchange* in 1915. The words are still true today some 80 years after they were written. Although the telephone has become an accepted part of our everyday lives, its introduction and early development in London, must be one of our best kept historical secrets.

London played host to the first public telephone exchange in the United Kingdom, but shamefully there is no published history currently available about the early days of the telephone system in the capital, in fact, books on the history of telecommunications in the U.K. are conspicuous by their absence. The most recent was published in 1947 under war-time paper restrictions without illustrations and is now out-of-print. The balance has been partly redressed by privately printed histories of the telephone's development in some large towns, but even copies of these books are now becoming difficult to obtain.

The reason behind this lack of printed material has not been due to complacency on the part of the historian, but because of the very nature of the subject. After all, it has only been in recent years that the telephone system has moved from a government department into the private sector of the market. This change has cut through some of the restraint on information imposed by department 'red tape', and made access to historical records very much easier than it had previously been.

My object is to present those early days of the telephone in the capital, how it grew and developed until 1912, when the National Telephone Company was taken over by the General Post Office. Through necessity of space I have restricted the geographical area covered to the family of exchanges whose forefathers were Messrs Edison and Bell. I have not included any of the early history of the Post Office Telephone system or the court battles that dogged the early development of the telephone in this country. The former would warrant a research of its own and the latter has already been documented in the books mentioned in the text.

Researching information for this book has been a long and arduous procedure, as there are no previous works to draw on except Baldwin's *History of the Telephone in the United Kingdom*. That has proved invaluable to me. For the most part I have had to follow clues from old house journals, annual general meeting reports, newspaper reports, telephone and street directories and a multitude of London histories. But most of all by using the historian's 'sixth sense'.

I would like to extend grateful thanks to the staff of B T Museum and B T Archives for their help and enthusiasm in my quest for information and the loan of photographs; the library staff of the Institute of Electrical Engineers, also the Royal Commission on the Historical Monuments of England and the London Guildhall Library, for access to their photographic collections.

Unfortunately, as with any research into the past, there are dark corners that defy investigation. My book contains its fair share of them. Though they will more than likely remain obscured forever, it is hoped that some light may filter through in the future.

To write about the telephone would be impossible without entering into some technical explanation, accordingly the format of the book should allow the more technical chapters to be over looked without losing too much of the historical value, although I have tried to explain technical detail as simply as possible.

I would like to think that my efforts have contributed a little more to the varied story of London's past and that you will gain as much enjoyment from reading these pages as I have had from writing them.

Dave Occomore - July 1994

Hawes Multiple Switchboard at Chancery Lane, with the new Western Electric Multiple Board in the background

THE BELL AND EDISON TELEPHONE COMPANY IN LONDON

The first practical telephone apparatus used in London consisted of two telephone instruments connected together by an iron wire strung across the roof tops and could only be used for simple inter-communication. For instance, a wire could connect a company's city office with its warehouses, or a gentleman's house and his stables. This limited use was not, of course, what Alexander Graham Bell envisaged for his invention, he was far sighted enough to realise that each owner of a telephone would sooner or later require inter-connection with others who owned a telephone. This requirement had already been called for in America and overcome by the adoption of a telegraph switching system, for the use of the telephone. This switching system was almost immediately available when the telephone was introduced on a commercial basis in London. Now that one caller could exchange conversation with another, a new word entered our vocabulary telephone 'Exchange'. Incidentally, the term 'subscriber' originated from these early days when customers subscribed an annual payment for the use of the company's facilities and unlimited

calls on their systems.

The first telephone exchange in London was situated at 36 Coleman Street at the offices of The Telephone Company Ltd. (Bell Patents). These offices were in a 4 storey building fronting Coleman Street. The Telephone Company, with James Brand as chairman, was formed by Colonel Reynolds from Providence, Rhode Island, on the 4th June, 1878. Colonel Reynolds had handled the early interests of the Bell Telephone in Great Britain and accompanied Alexander Graham Bell in the demonstration of the telephone to prominent people, including the royal family.

The Telephone Company (Bell) opened its first exchange in August, 1879, with 7 or 8 subscribers, who paid £20 a year for the privilege of being connected to the system. Quickly this number increased, an advert appearing in *The Globe*, 16th September, 1879; announced that The Telephone Company 'is already in successful operation, and a considerable number of the leading BANKERS, COMPANIES and MERCHANTS in the CITY are now connected through its Agency.' The company was so successful in fact, that two further exchanges were opened, one on the 3rd floor of a building called Leadenhall House, 101 Leadenhall Street. Described as; 'a grandiose high Victorian

3

block'[1] built in 1879 and encompassing eighty offices. The other was at Palace Chambers, Bridge Street, Westminster, of which only the ground and first floors still remain. This five floor Victorian building with handsome stone dressings was divided into forty or fifty single offices and stood opposite Westminster Clock Tower and the Houses of Parliament. The *Daily News* of 18th December, 1879, describes Leadenhall House as a 'central station' and Palace Chambers as a 'branch station'.

Almost immediately on the heels of the Telephone Company in London, Colonel Gouraud, then resident director of Mercantile Trust Company, and the London representative of the Edison telephone interests, formed the Edison Telephone Company of London on 2nd August, 1879. The company used Colonel Gouraud's office at 6 Lombard Street as their office, with the Rt Hon E P Bouverie as Chairman, to promote the Edison telephone commercially in the capital. The first Edison telephone exchange was an experimental affair at the 6 Lombard Street office. Trials started on 6th September, 1879, and were reported in the *Electrician* on 13th September, 1879, as follows :

4

On the 6th inst a private trial of the Edison telephone exchange took place at the company offices, Mansion House Chambers, Queen Victoria Street. The experiment embraced playing on the cornet from the exchange room in Lombard Street, singing and whistling tunes, speaking and whispering from the *Times* office in Queen Victoria Street and speaking and singing from other offices in Lombard Street, Copthall Buildings and Carey Street (Chancery Lane).

In the office a "stick" of matter was displayed which had been set up by a type composing machine at the *Times* office from the dictation of an Edison Telephone. From the offices in Mansion House Chambers there is at present communication with ten offices including the above, the most distant being Carey St. The various experiments appeared to be successful and as Mr Johnson who conducted them explained, if they can be carried out at ten offices *a fortiori* they can be carried out successfully at very many more. Mr Johnson is the chief engineer of the Edison Telephone Company, and Mr Edison's scientific representative in this country. Great merit is claimed for the instrument on account of being able to speak in a loud or soft voice with it so that what is said can be heard by a room full of people or by only one person and as we

The Silvertown telephone instrument with Blake transmitter as used by the Telephone Company, Ltd.

explained the instrument is purely mechanical controlled by electricity. After leaving the offices in Mansion House Chambers the party proceeded to the exchange in Lombard Street and were shown the different wires by means of which the experiment had been conducted and the practical working of them. There were in all twenty four distinct offices, twelve combinations could be made at one time a cross connection could be made with any two wires by which two offices could be placed in communication.

This test exchange was subsequently moved to the 2nd floor, 11 Queen Victoria Street, where the main Edison Company office was opened; in a large block of about 500 rooms called Mansion House Chambers, built in 1872 between Bucklersbury and Sise Lane, when Queen Victoria Street was laid out from Blackfriars to the Mansion House (destroyed in the 1941 air raids). The exact date of the move from Lombard Street to Queen Victoria Street is in some doubt. Baldwin in his *History of the telephone*, gives September, 1879, as the date, but the *Illustrated London News* of 15th November, 1879, still refers to Lombard Street as Edison's London exchange. To complicate matters more, the Post Office Archives have a newspaper cutting from the *Daily News* of

15th December, 1879, with an advert for the Edison Telephone Company London, Ltd, giving the central office as 11 Queen Victoria Street. A note attached to this from the Post Office Engineer-in-Chief's office dated 19th December, 1879, states that they may have moved to Queen Victoria Street from Lombard Street.

Business for the Edison Company, who incidentally were undercutting the Bell Company by £8, charging £12 per annum, was obviously on the increase, as the *Daily News* cutting quotes as branch stations: Westminster, Eastcheap, Temple, Cornhill, and Pall Mall, though the Post Office Engineer-in-Chief's office notes in fine copper plate hand:
18th December
I have been given to understand that exchanges have been opened at 77 Cornhill and 6 Lombard Street. The other places mentioned have not yet been established.

This is collaborated by an article in the *Standard*, 26th December, 1879; 'The existing London telephone lines extend already between Cornhill and Lombard Street and other local districts', although Baldwin writes: by the end of 1879 the Edison Company had opened up two further exchanges one in Eastcheap and the other in Chancery Lane. Personally, I think that the keen rivalry between the

Bell and Edison companies toward the end of 1879, together with the Edison company aggressive marketing, caused the Edison Company to promote some of their distant connections as 'branch stations' in the hope of attracting further business. A paragraph in the *Times* of 10th April, 1880, which I feel refers to the Edison Company (the Bell Company already had established an exchange opposite the Houses of Parliament at Westminster) goes some way toward clarifying the position :

Several chambers in the Temple will shortly possess the advantage of having communication by telephone with the law courts at Westminster and the Houses of Parliament. The telephonic apparatus is at present being laid down between the Temple Gardens and Westminster Hall, the Metropolitan District Railway being utilized for the purpose. The apparatus after having been connected with several of the chambers and offices in the Temple enters the underground railway line which is carried along immediately under the crown of the arch, until arriving at the subway leading into Palace Yard and is carried forward in the direction of Westminster Hall and the Houses of Parliament. Close to the spot where the telephone enters the railway a new lodge within the Temple grounds architecturally uniform with Harcote and Plowden buildings is in course of erection.

George Bernard Shaw, then in his early 20s, took a job as Wayleave Officer with the Edison Company in 1879. He described his experiences in the foreword of his novel, *The Irrational Knot*. Here he portrays the personality clash between the American and British personnel, employed in the Victorian days of the telephone industry in London. His comments go some way to explain the almost carnival antics adopted for testing the first Edison Exchange:

Whilst the Edison Telephone Company lasted, it crowded the basement of a high pile of offices in Queen Victoria Street with American artificers. These deluded and romantic men gave me a glimpse of the skilled proletariat of the United States. They sang obsolete sentimental songs of genuine emotion; and their language was frightful even to an Irishman. They worked with ferocious energy which was out of all proportion to the actual result achieved. Indomitably to assert their republican manhood by taking no orders from a tall-hatted Englishman, whose stiff politeness covered his conviction that they were, relatively to himself, inferior and common persons, they insisted on being slave driven with genuine American oaths by a genuine free and equal American foreman. They utterly despised the artfully slow British workman who did as little for his wages as he possibly could; never hurried himself; and had a deep reverence for any one whose pocket could be tapped by respectful behaviour. Need I add that they were contemptuously wondered at by this same British workman as a parcel of outlandish adult boys, who sweated themselves for their employer's benefit instead of looking after their own interests? They adored Mr Edison as the greatest man of all time in every possible department of science, art and philosophy, and execrated Mr Graham Bell, the inventor of the rival telephone, as his satanic adversary; but each of them held or intended to have on the brink of completion an improvement on the telephone, usually a new transmitter. They were free souled creatures, excellent company, sensitive, cheerful and profane; liars, braggarts and hustlers; with an air of making slow old England hum which never left them even when, as often happened, they were wrestling with difficulties of their own making, or struggling in no-thoroughfares from which they had to be retrieved like strayed sheep by Englishmen without imagination enough to go wrong.

The inability of the American staff to work with the British, is reflected on by J E Kingsbury, who later became the first agent and managing director of the Western Electric Co. in London. He began work with his uncle who ran an advertising agency in Georges Yard, Lombard Street, London, just round the corner from Colonel Gourand's office. In 1878 the Colonel, needing some assistance with the correspondence on his telephone and electric light interests, asked the agency if they could help, so Mr Kingsbury was sent along. He gained some practical experience of the telephone by helping to install them, although he could not get along with a technical expert who was sent over from America, as 'he seemed desirous of maintaining the exclusiveness of this information'.

Shaw maintained an interest in physics both by reading and through a friendship with a cousin of Graham Bell's in Ireland. This gave him some standing when it came to demonstrating the telephone. He continues: I was, I believe the only person in the entire establishment who knew the current scientific explanation of telephony; and as I soon struck up a friendship with our official lecturer - a Colchester man whose strong point was pre-scientific agriculture, I often discharged his duties for him in a manner which I'm persuaded laid the foundation of Mr Edison's

United Telephone Company wall type
instrument with Blake transmitter and
call bell in separate cases

London reputation; my sole reward
being my boyish delight in the
half-concealed incredulity of our
visitors (who were convinced by
the hoarsely startling utterances of
the telephone that the speaker,
alleged by me to be twenty miles
away, was really using a speaking
trumpet in the next room), and their
obvious uncertainty, when the
demonstration was over, as to
whether they ought to tip me or
not; a question they either decided
in the negative or never decided at
all, for I never got anything.

Kingsbury, on the other hand, gained his experience by simply having-a-go; to correct faults he had to conduct his own research and if the 'expert' was away and the telephone maintained a tactless silence he was generally appealed to for assistance and earned something of a reputation as a magician. He certainly proved to be a good engineer, if not a magician, as he went on to write four books on the telephone between 1882 and 1916.

A major drawback with the Bell and Edison company's equipment lay in the type of telephone instrument they were using at this time. The Telephone Co (Bell) possessed the patent rights to a most efficient telephone receiver. The same device was also used as a transmitter, but was by no means as efficient in this application. Eventually the Telephone Co replaced their magneto transmitter with one designed by Francis Blake and known as the Blake transmitter. This greatly improved the quality of transmission of the Telephone Co telephones. It was subsequently found to be useless in long distance transmission, but at this date it did not prove to be any problem. The new Telephone Co (Bell) telephones became known as 'Silvertown Sets' as they were manufactured at Silvertown by the India Rubber, Gutta Percha and Telegraph Works Co. The Edison telephone used a carbon transmitter and was very efficient giving good transmission; in fact, the carbon transmitter in various improved forms is still in use in most telephones today. The receiver for the Edison Telephone, was known by various names, 'motograph receiver', 'loud speaking receiver', or most commonly, 'the chalk receiver'. It worked very well, in fact so well that it became its own worst enemy, as the received conversation was broadcast to anyone who happened to be in the vicinity of the instrument allowing no privacy to the recipient of a telephone call. The other disadvantage to the Edison receiver from the subscriber's point of view was that during a conversation a handle had to be cranked to hear anything from the instrument. The two companies decided that the amalgamation of their interests would be the only answer to these technical difficulties, competition, and the ever increasing number of legal proceedings against patent infringement. Therefore a new company. The United Telephone Company, Ltd., was formed on 13th May, 1880, with Mr James Brand retained as chairman and an overall charge of £20 a year for subscribers.

1 London Before the Blitz   Richard Trench
Weidenfeld & Nicolson

THE TELEPHONE EXCHANGES
OF THE
UNITED TELEPHONE COMPANY
IN LONDON

Tracing the early years of the United Telephone Company in London has been particularly difficult. Finding the opening dates and addresses of its exchanges has not been easy, and in some cases was impossible. The United listed its exchanges, or 'exchange stations' in the front of its early telephone directories. But this was by no means a clear indication that these stations were working switchrooms at the time of publication. Clarifying the position with street directories of the day has again run into some difficulty, as there seemed to be some reluctance on the part of the United to have all their exchanges listed. This, I suspect, was due to the company trying to maintain some anonymity, as its relations with the telephone using public were not of the best and so it didn't want to encourage a stream of customers knocking on the exchange door demanding better service.

The earliest dated telephone directory which has survived was issued on 26th April, 1880, by the Telephone Company Ltd (Bell) just prior to the United Telephone Company's formation. The directory indicates that there were Bell exchanges in London at Leadenhall Street, Hop Exchange Southwark, Westminster (Palace Chambers), Coleman Street, Lawcourt Chambers 40 Chancery Lane, Leather Exchange Bermondsey, and East India Avenue. Of these it appears that the Lawcourt Chambers and Leather Exchange were only projected and were never opened, although the latter was still listed in the United Telephone Company directory of 23rd August, 1880. Hop and East India Avenue exchanges were opened at a later date. The Edison Telephone Company also printed a list of subscribers, from the imprint it may have been issued in March, 1880. Its exchanges are given as Central Exchange, 11 Queen Victoria Street and Branch City exchanges at 77 Cornhill, 34 Eastcheap (3rd floor Worcester House), Lonsdale Chambers Chancery Lane (4th floor 27 Chancery Lane), and 3, 4, 5, Windmill Street.

The number of exchanges operated by the United Telephone Company at its formation is given by Baldwin as eight: 36 Coleman Street, Leadenhall Street, Westminster, (all from the Bell company). 11 Queen Victoria Street, 77 Cornhill, Eastcheap, 27 Chancery Lane, and Heddon Street, (from the former Edison company). In the early directories an exchange was listed at 3, 4, 5 Windmill Street (now Lexington Street), but

Queen Victoria Street looking east from St Mary Aldermary, c.1910. Bank Exchange on right hand side in distance with overhead cables crossing street to the Exchange

this had the same number range as Heddon Street, the name changing between June and August, 1881. This was probably the first exchange transfer to take place in London. The directory for October, 1880, lists exchanges at East India Dock and Temple. In the January, 1881, edition Temple had one subscriber and an exchange called Shadwell was added to the list. By April, 1881, both Temple and Shadwell had been deleted, any subscribers that might have been connected to these exchanges would have been dispersed to others.

Baldwin goes on to say that: 'applications for telephone service were now being received from numerous quarters and it was evidently possible to secure remunerative business in other parts of the metropolis as yet untouched by the extension of the facilities for exchange service further afield. The United Company therefore decided to open additional telephone exchanges in various parts of London... the necessary arrangements were quickly made, suitably situated premises were secured and exchanges appeared to have been opened in the following order before the end of 1882

Firstly, 6 East India Avenue. East India Avenue (now demolished), was built on the site of East India House that housed the offices of the old East India Company, the exchange later became known only as Avenue.

Secondly, Commercial Sale Rooms, Mincing Lane. The building was erected in 1859-60 upon land belonging to the Grocers' Company, especially as offices and sample rooms for merchants and Colonial firms dealing in tea, sugar, coffee, cocoa, raisins, dates, rice, spices and similar goods. The building contained a fine marble hall and 200 business offices.

Thirdly, Hop Exchange. Hop telephone exchange was established in the Hop and Malt Exchange (offices number 84 - 85) in Southwark Street where trading in hops, malt and seed was carried on. The central area of the Hop exchange was spanned by a cast iron and glass roof that surmounted four stories of offices and showrooms the three upper floors were connected by a cast iron gallery running round the inside of the building. Eventually the building was gutted by fire on October 20th, 1920, long after the telephone exchange now known as 'Hop' had moved.

Fourthly, 67 Cow Cross Street, Smithfield. This exchange was sited very near the District and Metropolitan railway station at Farringdon Road.

Fifth, Kings Cross at 249 Pentonville Road.

Sixth, East India Dock. An exchange, East India Dock (no address given), was listed in the

United Telephone Directories from 1880. In 1881 this exchange was either moved or enlarged, however from then on it was located in the attic of the Eastern Hotel, Limehouse (now demolished) on the intersection of East and West India Dock Roads and became known as Eastern and then East.

Seventh and last, Edgware Road.

It must be remembered that Baldwin compiled his list over forty years after the events described and probably relied on his own and his contemporaries' memories for much of his information, so it is not surprising that some inaccuracy may of occurred. By looking at the evidence of the early telephone directories the number range for Kings Cross does not appear listed until February, 1884. The exchange name is not given neither are any subscribers listed, so we must assume that the exchange must have opened later than 1882. We know that Edgware Road exchange opened in 1883 as the opening was announced in *The Electrician*[1]. The United Telephone Company's annual general meeting report of July, 1882, records; seven exchanges were opened in 1880, four more in 1881, and three, together with Smithfield, in 1882, making fifteen in all. A look at Baldwin's list and a further check in the directories leads me to believe that the seven exchanges referred to as opening in 1880 by the board, were the original 1879/80 Bell and Edison exchanges except Heddon Street. Hop, East India Avenue, Heddon Street and Eastern, were the four opened in 1881. Although Windmill Street and East India Dock were listed before 1881 it is possible that the board did not recognise them as exchanges until they became known as Heddon Street and Eastern. Smithfield appears last in the list of the August, 1882, directory; the three exchanges named immediately above it are London Dock & Shadwell, Stratford, and Victoria Dock. This would then be consistent with the figures given to the annual general meeting in 1882. None of the early directories show Mincing Lane as an exchange, but as Baldwin gives the same exchange numbers in his book as those for East Cheap in the directories, I can only conclude that somewhere between 1883 and 1884 the Eastcheap exchange was moved to Mincing Lane, but retained its old name. The United Telephone Company at Worcester House, 34 East Cheap, is listed in the Post Office Street Directory until 1884 and pictured in the Graphic in September 1883[2].

The reported improvements to the telephone system under the United were also noted by *The Electrician*[3]

Improved Telephonic Communication

The United Telephone Company have established offices in Lonsdale Chambers, Chancery Lane and at the Metropolitan Railway Station at Westminster Bridge. So that direct communication is now available between the Law Courts and Westminster.

The Bell and Edison systems were now interconnected.

With all this activity going on it was not surprising that the United Telephone Company soon found itself with a rival, in the form of the London and Globe Telephone and Maintenance Company Ltd. It was formed in 1881, with a head office at Telephone Building, 31 Queen Victoria Street. They undercut the United's tariff by half, charging only £10 a year. They set up their exchange in premises at the Wool Exchange, Basinghall Street. The Wool Exchange was very much like the Hop Exchange in south London and was described as 'Victorian and pretentious, a palazzo of glass and marble.'[4] Behind the wrought iron gate a passage led to the domed octagonal hall in a glazed court, the hall being linked to the buildings around by iron walkways. Wool dealers had come here since 1875, spending mornings at the London docks inspecting wool from Australia, New Zealand, Argentina and the Falklands, and the afternoons at the exchange.

The rivalry between the two companies was very bitter, to say the least. As the Coleman Street exchange was only a street away from the Globe Company exchange, many of the United's wires already crossed the roof of the Wool Exchange and so the Globe demanded they be removed. The United didn't take a great deal of notice, after all they were there first. The Globe Company then lassoed wires across the United's, shorting them out, and at times connected their battery or ringing current to them, causing the United's subscribers bells to ring and annoying the operators in the United's switchrooms. James Reynolds a Globe Company labourer, said, "The men had a laugh about it on the roof, as they knew what the result would be."[5] All kinds of allegations and counter-charges, as to this tying up and cutting of wires, were lodged by both companies' employees, eventually leading to a court case. As the hearing approached the Globe began to take photographs to present as evidence to the court. Mr Clay, who was then chief of the United Telephone Company's instrument department, thought that the photographs could give a misleading view of the circum-stances as it was quite possible to show the wires in contact or not according to the position from which the photographs were taken.

Leadenhall House, Leadenhall Street in 1899. The telephone exchange was installed on the third floor

16

He proposed that a model of all the roof tops surrounding the Wool Exchange should be made and obtained authority to undertake the work in conjunction with an architect. After two days however, the architect gave up, scrambling over roof tops to obtain measurements was too much for him. So Mr Clay with the help of two other engineers of the telephone company continued the work and subsequently appeared at the Guildhall to explain the model in court. It was soon realised that the lawyers acting for both parties were the only financial winners in this battle and so the matter was eventually settled by the United acquiring the Globe for £25,000 on the 24th June, 1884. The Globe Telephone Company switchboard in the Wool Exchange was shut and, as most of the Globe's subscribers were duplicated on the United Company's system, it was simple to divert the balance to other United Telephone exchanges.

In these early days of the telephone system in London all the exchanges were connected to each other. Providing all the overhead cables and wires proved extremely costly. An expense that would increase as the system grew. Also it was uneconomical from the operating point of view, as many of these lines between exchanges would be lying idle for long periods. In order to facilitate better inter-exchange connections a central trunk exchange was opened in 1883 at Oxford Court, Cannon Street, to which exchanges were connected.[6]

The growth of the United Telephone Company continued at a rapid pace. In July 1883[7] the company reported to its share-holders:

'since 30th April [1883] we have opened the Millwall Exchange and an exchange at the Edgware Road and there are one or two on the point of being opened'.[8]

The Edgware Road exchange was situated on the top floor over a tobacconist's shop at 45 Burne Street, on the corner of Chapel Street,[9] opposite the Metropolitan District Line Underground Railway Station. The 1884 street directory lists the proprietor as J Berman.

By the end of 1888 the United Telephone Company had closed a number of minor London exchanges and gradually centralized their system. The exact dates for all the changes are not known, but it seems reasonable to conclude the following.

At the eighth annual general meeting of the United Telephone Company in 1888[10] the report to shareholders announced the closure of the Leadenhall Street, Stratford and Shadwell exchanges. (I think Victoria Dock should have been included). These closures were probably completed in March, as a

Oxford Court Telephone Exchange, Cannon Street

18

report in the *Weekly Bulletin* of 31st March, 1888, warns the public:

The United Telephone Company announces that their City exchanges will be closed at 2pm on Saturday the 31st instead of at 5pm as usual as they propose taking advantage of the Easter Holiday to make certain improvements and alterations in their switchrooms.

Subscribers on Leadenhall Street exchange were transferred to Coleman Street and those on Stratford and Shadwell (Victoria Dock) to Eastern exchange, Limehouse. Millwall had in all probability been moved to Eastern some time before this date. In November, 1889, Coleman Street exchange was moved to larger accommodation, taking over the old Globe premises at the Wool Exchange where a new switchboard had been installed. Eastern exchange was also enlarged after 1884, using the old exchange equipment from the now defunct

Globe Telephone Company This was probably installed at 14, West India Dock Road, in premises that eventually became a German Seaman's Home in 1908.

1 *The Electrician* 28th July, 1883, p 261.
2 Baldwin's statement; "Exchanges appeared to have been opened in the following order before the end of 1882," may have been an oversight and should have read 1883 or 84. This would have been more consistent with the evidence uncovered.
3 *The Electrician* 2nd July, 1881.
4 London before the Blitz Richard Trench.
5 *The Electrician* 19th May, 1883.
6 *National Telephone Journal (NTJ)* June, 1909 p 60.
7 *The Electrician* July, 1883.
8 According to early Telephone Directories, there was a Millwall Exchange listed from 6th August 1881. It is possible that Millwall was moved in 1883 into the Eastern Hotel, alongside Eastern Exchange. This would explain the entry in the *Electrician*, also the directories list Millwall as a separate number range until early 1883. From June, 1883, and subsequent directories exchange names were abandoned and from this point the number ranges of the two exchanges appear to be listed sequential as a single exchange (Eastern).
9 Only a short stub of Burne Street remains. The major part was swallowed up by the Edgware Road flyover and the extension of Harrow Road.
10 *Financial News* 4th July, 1888.

Globe Telephone Company interfering with United Telephone Company lines

THE SWITCHBOARDS OF THE UNITED TELEPHONE COMPANY

At the centre of the early telephone exchange was the 'switchboard,' that housed the keys (switches) and cords, used by an operator to connect the telephone lines of the company's subscribers.

The first switchboard used in London was at the Telephone Company's (Bell) exchange at 36 Coleman Street. This board was curiously called a "slipper jack board", and had only two working positions, but needed three or four people to operate it. Two answering operators sat at tables equipped with a telephone transmitter and receiver and a number of keys (switches), while the other one or two, connecting operators stood at a vertical panel, where calls could be set up by flexible cords. One end of each of these cords was terminated with a metal blade set in a handle made of insulating material. The blade and the handle resembled a 'jack knife' this was clipped under a spring or 'slipper' on the face of the vertical panel, hence the name 'slipper jack'.

To make a call, the subscriber pressed a calling button, thus extending current from a battery associated with his telephone instrument, over a single wire to an indicator on the vertical panel of the switchboard. Here the connecting operator slipped the blade or jack, of one of the cords, into the corresponding slipper. The other end of the cord terminated within a brass peg, which was then inserted in a hole in a brass strip, so putting the caller in contact with the answering operator seated at the table. Once this operator established to whom the caller wished to be connected, he had to call out the details to the connecting operator at the panel. The latter used a second cord to connect the calling, and the called, subscribers together. The only way that the answering operator knew a call had finished, was to monitor the circuit at intervals to see if conversation had ceased. Once this had happened, the answering operator had to tell the connecting operator to remove the cords connecting the call from the panel.

The first switchboard at Coleman Street, and possibly the switchboard at Palace Chambers, Westminster, were known as Williams Switchboards and were probably manufactured in America by Charles Williams of Boston[1]. The slipperjack switchboard that was installed at Leadenhall Street, was made at Silvertown by the India Rubber, Gutta Percha and Telegraph Works Company and worked in conjunction with their Silvertown telephone sets. This board was provided with a galvanometer which showed when the calling subscriber replaced his receiver, obviating the necessity of the answering operator having to monitor the calls.

The switchboard used by the Edison Company was designed on a different principle from the Bell slipperjack board. The main part of this board consisted of a matrix of horizontal and vertical brass bars. Here the interconnection of the subscriber and answering operator, was effected by inserting a brass peg into the appropriate crossing point of the bars. A subscriber wishing to make a call operated a calling key on his telephone instrument, thereby dropping an indicator on which his number appeared at the switchboard. The

answering operator could then connect to the incoming call, by positioning a brass peg in an appropriate crossing point. When he stated the number required a further peg was used to connect the parties together, the operator restoring the indicator by hand. At the end of the call, one or other of the subscribers used his calling key to operate the indicator a second time, thereby signalling to the operator that the call had finished.

With the formation of the United Telephone Company, Baldwin states that further switchboards were installed at the following places: Mincing Lane, Smithfield, and Edgware Road. These were of the slipperjack type, with Avenue,

Slipper jack switchboard, Palace Chambers, Westminster, 1883

The Edison switchboard at Hop Exchange, Southwark Street

Hop, King's Cross, and East, of the Edison variety. He continues:

It is not clear whether the excess of Edison over slipperjack switchboards in use in London at this time may be taken as an indication that the performance of the Edison board was considered generally to be superior to that of the slipper board; probably the question of facility for securing early delivery had something to do with the selection, nevertheless at this time the Edison board, in so far as its use in London was concerned, was in the ascendancy.

Whatever the reason, the Edison board appears from this distance in time to have been the easier to operate.

With the expansion of the telephone service in London, it became necessary to provide more than one switchboard at an exchange. Switchboards began to be placed side-by-side, or in the case of the Edison boards also above and below, according to the requirements of the exchange. Although these additional switchboards were interconnected, the subscribers only had one appearance at the exchange. As long as the two subscribers who required connection to each other were on the same operating position of the switchboard, one operator could deal with the call. If they appeared on different positions the necessary particulars, as to whether the subscribers were 'engaged' or 'free', to take a call, had to be verbally passed between the operators. At busy times a state of near pandemonium ensued, while operators shouted instructions to each other.

In the *National Telephone Journal* for April, 1909, one solution to this problem was recorded:

It will be readily appreciated that in a large exchange of, say, 500 lines this system of every operator calling across the room for local numbers, and to the 'trunk' or junction operators for their numbers on other exchanges, was not conductive to quiet and smooth working, especially when, as it frequently happened, only one strip was disengaged and the operator to whom you were calling also wanted the strip for an incoming connection; a battle royal would occasionally ensue, which would only probably be settled by an appeal to the clerk-in-charge. To minimise this trouble, Mr Sandy, who was then the clerk-in-charge of Mincing Lane Exchange, which was I believe, the largest exchange built on this principle, introduced the idea of having an operator or boy messenger whose sole duty it was to walk about the switchroom making local connections; this greatly reduced the evil.

Miss Ellen Ralph who joined the United in March, 1882, as an operator at Avenue Exchange comments :

To obtain connection, either local or on the junction lines ('trunks' as they were then called), the operators had to shout to each other, and apparently those with the strongest lungs were, under the peculiar conditions, able to make the quickest connections[1].

The problem continued for a good number of years, until these switchboards were replaced. Miss Ada Knapman who started as an operator in January, 1892, recalled her first day at Hop Exchange, where she had to wait for some considerable time outside the building, the noise inside drowned her brother's knocks at the door and finally they had to open the door and introduce themselves to the clerk-in-charge[2].

To overcome the working difficulties operators experienced on these early switchboards, Mr Hawes, a United Telephone Company electrician, designed a switchboard that allowed the operator to check that a particular line was 'free,' or 'engaged'. His idea was very simple: subscribers' jacks (by now the modern meaning of the term jack i.e. the socket that a plug pushes into, was in use) were given an appearance on each position, along a line of switchboards, a system that became known as the 'Multiple system'. At the same time it was arranged for

The first western Electric upright multiple switchboard in London at 11 Queen Victoria Street

each appearance to have a test stud. An operator, by touching the test stud with a thimble on her finger connected to a buzzer, could hear if a line was in use, or in technical parlance, 'engaged'. For answering purposes each position had a number of subscribers allotted to it, they appeared on indicators very similar to those on the earlier slipperjack boards. Even on this multiple switchboard there was still no clearing indication given to the operator, she had to rely on her test stud to check for the termination of the call. An unusual feature of Mr Hawes multiple switchboard was the jack field, this was arranged horizontally not vertically as the old Bell slipper and

Edison switchboards, this gave rise to the affectionate name of the 'Hawes Trough'. Only two of these boards were installed, both at London exchanges. Oxford Court, brought into service in 20th November, 1883, and Chancery Lane early in 1884. Further development by Mr Hawes of this type of switchboard was prevented in England by patents taken out by Western Electric Company. They had been working on the same operating problems in the States and, unknown to Mr Hawes, had produced a multiple switchboard of their own design.

The first Western Electric upright multiple board to come into service in Britain was in Liverpool in

From *The Graphic*, 1 September, 1883. Top middle: Slipper jack board in switchroom, Westminster. Lower middle: Edison board in switchroom, Eastcheap. Top left & right: Conversation between London and Brighton. Lower left: 36 Coleman Street. Lower right: Reporter at House of Commons

1884, finally coming to London in 1888, where the Edison switchboard at 11, Queen Victoria Street, was replaced. Each section of this switchboard comprised three operator positions, each equipped with ten pairs of plugs and cords, with associated keys, ring off indicators to tell the operator a call had finished, and calling indicators. Both of these had to be restored manually by the operator. There was also, of course, the subscriber's multiple. At first these boards were wired for earth return (earth circuit boards), but gradually, where they were still in use, they were modified for metallic return working. They were also originally provided with battery ringing, for operating the D.C. trembler bells associated with the subscriber's instrument. This system was then replaced by magneto signalling (A.C. ringing current)[2]. A generator supplied ringing current to the ring key, on the operator's position of the exchange switchboard. The operator used a Blake transmitter, that hung in front of the switchboard on an adjustable bracket. The first of these switchboards had the transmitters fitted into a wooden box, but in later boards they were in slimmer nickel plated cases, both versions were paired with a hand-held receiver.

To explain the working of a Multiple Magneto exchange, I can do no better than quote from the first hand knowledge of Mr Hall Ellis[3]

The switchboard is constructed in sections. The lower part of a section provides three operating 'positions', while the upper part consists of five panels which accommodate strips of jacks. Each operator had before her 'position equipment', which, from bottom to top, consisted of a key shelf, subscribers' indicators and cord shelf. Calls were connected by means of flexible cords, arranged in pairs one behind the other. Corresponding to each pair of cords was a three position key on the key shelf below. Inside the switchboard the cords hung downwards, returning behind in a loop to about the same level. A weighted pulley pulled the cord down when it was out of use, until the plug at the end of the cord was resting on the cord shelf. The three positioned key when in its normal upright position disconnected the two cords of the cord circuit from the operators instrument. Pushed forward, it enabled her to hear and speak on a connection, and pulled towards the operator, it connected ringing current to the subscriber's line. The panels which formed the upper part of the switchboard contained many strips of jacks. Five strips, one above the other, and each containing twenty jacks, formed a block of a hundred in the exchange numeration. The number of the hundred was shown by a label on the 'stile strip' on its left. Cables ran to the multiple jacks, and the blocks of a hundred ran in sequence from left to right so as to occupy the five panels of a section in layers running from bottom to top. Having served one set of jacks in this way, the cabling ran on to provide another appearance on the next section, and so on round the entire switchboard. By this means, every number of the exchange was accessible to every operator. When a subscriber wished to make a call, he turned the handle of a magneto generator which formed part of his instrument. The current from the generator passed through the coil of an electro-magnet in his indicator on the switchboard. This caused an armature to vibrate, and a latch on one end of the armature released a shutter of the indicator, which fell down and signalled the call to the operator. To answer the call, she took the plug of the more distant 'answering' cord of a free pair, and inserted it in an answering jack corresponding to the indicator, situated at the bottom of one of the panels on her position. She restored the indicator by hand, and answered the subscriber by throwing the speaking key proper to the cord circuit. The subscriber stated what number he wanted and the operator used the nearer

Edison switchboard at the United Telephone Company's Avenue Exchange

'calling' cord of the pair to connect him. The operator first tested to see if the required number was already engaged. She did this by touching the bush of the multiple jack with the tip of her calling plug. If the number was engaged on a call, there must of necessity be a plug in one of the required subscriber's jacks somewhere else on the switchboard, and this produced an electrical condition on the bushes of all the other jacks which caused a click in her receiver. If the called number were free, the operator plugged into the multiple jack and gave a ring by pulling the key backwards. When the subscriber had finished speaking, the caller was supposed to 'ring ~ off' with his generator. This time an indicator dropped which was associated with the cord circuit, and the operator took down the connection. Often, however, the subscriber would forget to give the clearing signal, and so the operator needed to monitor her connections frequently to see which calls had ended.

It was from the days of the magneto switchboard that the saying 'I'll ring off' originated. Also if a subscriber on the magneto exchange became impatient, and tried to attract the attention of the called party by turning his magneto generator he would drop the clearing indicator and would be disconnected by the operator.

Soon these switchboards were fitted to other London exchanges; Cornhill came next and then at Chancery Lane, where the new switchboard was provided behind the old Hawes multiple board. Smithfield, East India Avenue and, finally, a replacement to Westminster, where the opportunity to move from the, by now, cramped Palace Chambers building to a new site at 6 Victoria Street was taken. The new exchange was brought into service on 24th November, 1888.

The old switchboard equipment recovered from the Globe Company at the Wool Exchange was put to use as a replacement of the Bell slipper jack switchboard, in the attic of the Eastern Hotel. The empty premises at the Wool Exchange, Basinghall Street, were then taken for a Western Electric multiple switchboard to replace the old Coleman Street slipper-jack exchange which was now well out of date.

1 Baldwin p 26.
2 *NTJ* July, 1907 p 75
3 *NTJ* Nov, 1908 p 174.
4 Generator ringing was invented by Thos Watson, Bell's assistant in 1878. A very important invention for telephony, as no DC path in the telephone instrument was required for ringing.
5 *The Early Years of the Telephone Service in Bristol, 1879-1931*. Mr Hall Ellis. British Telecom Publication.

THE UNITED TELEPHONE COMPANY'S OVERHEAD WIRES AND CABLES

The switchboard in the telephone exchange was connected to the subscriber's telephone instrument by a single wire, using an earth return to complete the circuit. These wires were supported by wooden and iron poles attached to the roof-tops, And where they converged on the exchange roof they were terminated on what was termed a 'derrick'. A description of the roof derrick at Avenue exchange appeared in the *Pall Mall Gazette* in December, 1883:

From the lofty roof of one of the houses of that sombre court rises a derrick, a square structure of wrought-iron bars 30 or 40 feet high by 8 to 10 feet wide, and looking like the upper portion of a skeleton lighthouse, very rigid and very transparent. This edifice is surmounted by a lighting conductor; you ascend it by a perpendicular ladder, and, pausing on its upper story, for it is divided into two floors, you look round from your airy perch to find that what appears innumerable wires radiate from your transparent cage in every possible direction over the dirty house-tops of the City. Most of these wires are bare and unenclosed; others are in cables containing each twenty wires. Each of them is lettered and numbered, and a cupboard on the derrick contains an apparatus for testing them.[1]

From here the wires were led down to the switchroom below. The overhead wires first used in London were 3/16 stranded galvanised iron, they were attached to the upright poles one above the other on shackle insulators. The lead in wires to the subscribers' premises and exchanges, were of 18/7½ gutta percha insulated copper wire. Early overhead cables were made by binding together by hand a number of these gutta percha insulated wires with a prepared tape. As the numbers of wires carried by roof poles increased more substantial cables were formed by inserting a 3/16 galvanised wire in the centre of a bundle of 30 insulated wires that were again bound together.

Baldwin reports the arrangement of connecting the subscribers' wires to the switchroom at Coleman Street and Avenue exchanges:

At 36 Coleman Street, the gutta percha insulated wires, which were employed for leading in the subscribers' lines from the open wires to the exchange, were at first terminated direct upon the switchboard; but, as the number of incoming lines increased, the need for intermediate testing facilities became apparent, and was provided in the form of a large square board of teak, fixed vertically, through which large brass terminals were fitted two inches apart (5cm). The single gutta percha-covered leads from the roof structure were terminated on the one side, and, from the other, cables made up of single cotton covered paraffined wires bound together to form a cable, were run to the switchboard. This arrangement provided the facilities desired, but, in course of time, additional wires were provided and the mass of insulated conductors terminated on the line side of the terminal board became very bulky, so that access to the terminals on the upper portion became well-nigh impossible.

Consequently, when it was decided to provide similar facilities for the Avenue exchange a different and improved device was adopted. The arrangement was situated immediately below the roof, and consisted of two long boards fixed horizontally and parallel one above the other. On the upper board the leads from the roof standard, and on the lower the wires from the switchboard, were terminated on terminals in rows of ten deep, cross connecting wires being run between them as required. In this manner the first form of telephone cross-connecting frame or test-board in London came into being.

With the steady growth of the telephone system in London, fears were raised in many quarters as to the safety of an expanding network

Exchange derrick at Bank, showing cables running across roof-tops from Oxford Court Exchange, 1909

Tubular steel derrick at Coleman Street. These were replaced by the more substantial iron plate type

of overhead wires and cables, Baldwin continues:

In the course of a very few years from the inception of the telephone in London, when the business had become firmly established, the rapidly increasing number of overhead wires, and the introduction and employment of aerial cables erected across principal thoroughfares of the city, began to excite public notice and comment. The unsightliness and alleged danger of the network of overhead wires above the streets and upon the roofs of the city became the subject of lengthy and frequent comment in the technical and general press, and the outcry against these wires soon became universal. Various views and opinions were expressed as to the wisdom of permitting telephone companies to work their unfettered will above the public thoroughfares in such a manner, and suggestions were made that there should be control by some authoritative body. Questions were raised as to whether the public authorities already possessed powers which would enable them to enforce some measure of control over the companies, and compel them to obtain permission for the erection of wires over, along, or across public thoroughfares. Stories of accidents to pedestrians and others from falling wires were not lacking and fears were expressed that every street in the city would soon become covered with a dense cobweb or a huge gridiron of wires, and the wanton and insolent aggressiveness of the telephone companies in the matter was noted.

Fears about the dangers of overhead wires were voiced in the London press[2]:

It is true, comparatively few serious accidents have been brought to the notice of the public; but they have already been frequent and serious, and these will be considerably augmented when the wires have become corroded and worn; the writer continues, Look, for instance, at the Coleman Street Station, and imagine the result of a fire there which would destroy the supports and suffer the wires to fall in every direction, seriously damaging the property over which they pass and most effectually blocking every thoroughfare to say nothing of the inevitable loss of life.

One particular London resident took action to prevent wires from crossing a communal garden[3].

Sitting yesterday morning in my room which gives on a garden held in common with some twenty neighbours who surround it I saw a man with a coil of wire outside. On enquiring I found him to be in the employ of a telephone company and to be instructed to put up a telephone from the house of a gentleman resident in South Kensington to his place of business and that in pursuance of this object he was carrying the wire between two houses to which he had permission to attach it in such a manner that it would span the garden in mid-air. I naturally objected to an erection interfering with the safe enjoyment of our garden and with the assistance of two of my neighbours finally succeeded in having the wire removed - had not my two neighbours and I been on the spot and taken hold of the wire and hitched it on an area grating, the excellent workmen in obedience to their orders would in a trice have swung it up far above our heads leaving us below to get our remedy as we could; the company has given in and proposed the alternative plan to carry the wire over the tops of our houses which in case of fracture would break the fall.   Alfred Bonham-Carter

In May, 1884, the Board of Works for the Wandsworth District applied to the courts for an injunction to restrain the United Telephone Company from retaining, or placing, any wire over, along, or across any street under their control without their consent. The injunction was granted but reversed in the Court of Appeal, on the grounds that the wires did not interfere with the use of the streets below. This allowed the company to continue to run wires across the streets, as long as they were constructed in a 'safe and proper manner'. In the same year the United Telephone Company tried to pass a bill through Parliament to allow them to put telephone wires under the streets and maintain posts along any street, but the bill was opposed and had to be withdrawn. So the company continued to rely on wayleave agreements with private property owners to develop the telephone system.

The overhead wires of the telephone network were vulnerable to storms and fires, the risk increasing every year, as the spread of cables and wires increased.

On 25th December, 1886, there was a severe snow storm in London that wreaked havoc with the overhead wires, cables and poles. The snow partially melted and then froze and in the following gale the strain on the wires and cables bent or broke many wooden and iron poles and their supports. The exchange derricks at Oxford Court, and Mincing Lane were torn from the roof and fell into the street. The scene in London was described in a letter to the *Times*.[4]

Anyone who walks about London today will see if he directs his attention from the slush in the streets hundreds and hundreds of overhead wires which have succumbed, like the cedars and other trees in our gardens, from the

Fire damage at Heddon Street with Exchange derrick collapsed into the street

effect of last night's snowfall.
Both in the City and the West End great has been the destruction. Broken and bent telegraph posts on the roofs, wires rolled up and put away in corners with ends hanging or tied round railings or lamp posts are visible in all directions. Telephone and telegraph communications have been materially interrupted in the metropolis as well as throughout the country. The expense of reinstatement of these posts and wires will necessarily be considerable and there will be the same liability to destruction when four inches of snow again falls suddenly.

H W Tyler, Carlton Club, Pall Mall.

Beatrice Newman, who was an operator at the time of the storm recalled: When the operators returned after the Christmas holidays (the exchanges were closed during holidays in those days), they found the poles and wires had been so heavily damaged that, so far as their work was concerned, there was scarcely any to do, for which she was afraid they were not properly sorry, and for quite an interval telephone users must have been compelled to resort to the old methods of sending messages by hand or letter.[5]

At the United Telephone Company's annual general meeting in 1888 the shareholders were told that iron derricks to replace those lost in the snow storm had been erected at Oxford Court, Queen Victoria Street, Mincing Lane, East India Avenue, Cornhill, Hop, Smithfield and one was in preparation for Heddon Street. These derricks were of a more substantial construction than their predecessors. Instead of forming a square of braced iron poles the replacements, although still square, were of riveted iron plates.

1 Baldwin p 57
2 *The Standard* 31st Jan, 1882.
3 *The Times* 29th Nov, 1883.
4 *The Times* 29th Dec, 1886.
5 *NTJ* Nov, 1907 p 160.

Clerks in Charge at a 'Telephone Women' Officers meeting, 1909. Back row (l-r): Miss Ralph, Metropolitan Operating School; Miss MacLachlan, Burnley; Miss Hall, Sunderland; Miss Ferguson, Edinboro'; Miss Butcher, London Wall; Miss Richards, Gerrard; Miss Law, Leicester. Front: Miss Harper, Bournemouth; Mrs Peters, Glasgow; Miss Minter, London; Miss Jinkins, Plymouth

WORKING IN EARLY TELEPHONE EXCHANGES

OPERATORS AND ENGINEERS OF THE UNITED TELEPHONE COMPANY

The United Telephone Company, like many industries in the late Victorian period, has not passed any records of its employees down for future study. All that is given are tantalising glimpses of those early days in short biographical vignettes of their senior male Engineers and the female Clerks-in-Charge who had overall responsibility for the girls in the switchroom. From these sources I have been able to extract some details to give an impression of working life with the United Telephone Company.

When telephone exchanges were first opened in London, they were not staffed twenty four hours a day, but gradually their opening time was extended:

The fusion of the late Bell and Edison Companies is complete and henceforth the Metropolitan Exchange Stations will be open from 9 a m to 7 p m, except Saturday, when the hours will be from 9 a m to 5 p m.[1]

Miss Ellen Ralph remembered the shifts that those early operators were working and the difficulties of weekend connections :

The hours for operators from 1881 to 1886 were from nine to six and ten to seven; after this came twelve to eight, and later twelve to nine. Subscribers who wished specially for later service, such as the press, were left connected by special switches, and woe betide the responsible operator if she forgot them. On one occasion, Miss Ralph, being that unfortunate person, dreamed one Saturday night that she had not turned them, and went to the exchange on Sunday to see if this was true; luckily it was only a dream. A less fortunate girl at Westminster actually did forget a particularly troublesome subscriber, and went to the exchange at two o'clock in the morning to put matters right, having to ring the night watchman.[2]

Miss Emily Richards was one of the first operators employed on all night service, when it was started in February, 1885, at Westminster and Heddon Street. These two particular exchanges being selected as it was considered the service might be found useful by Members of Parliament. One of the two "Lady Inspectresses" was on duty at each exchange, Miss Richards being the operator selected for Heddon Street. On the first night only one call was made from the House of Commons to the Constitutional Club, the remainder of the small hours being occupied in driving mice from the exchange, which they had apparently hitherto looked upon as their happy hunting ground, and possibly resented the intrusion of "night staff.[3] "The United Telephone Company Directory of September, 1885, lists the following hours for London exchange service.

All the exchanges are open daily for the transmission of messages from 9 a m to 9 p m, excepting on Sundays, Christmas Day, Good Friday, Bank Holidays, and any holidays specially authorised by the Directors. The West End exchanges are open all night, that is, there is a continuous service at these exchanges by day and by night, excepting Sundays and the other days already mentioned, on which days all the exchanges are closed.

At first, boys were employed in telephone exchanges, as operators in the switchrooms. Charles Sibley started work with The Telephone Company in 1879. His earliest experience was in working the first Bell switchboard installed in this country and after spending a short period in the mechanics' shop, he was sent to make himself acquainted with the Edison boards while they were in use at Cornhill, and Queen Victoria Street, exchanges. He was subsequently promoted to Clerk-in-Charge at Leadenhall House and Smithfield exchanges.[4] Upon the formation of the United Telephone Company and the appointment of Mr Bond Morgan as managing director, boys were gradually replaced by women operators who were far more suited to the type of work involved.[5] In the *Cassell's Family Magazine* for 1883 the following letter appears:

TELEPHONE WORK AS EMPLOYMENT FOR LADIES.

Sir, Among the many occupations that have during the last few years presented themselves for ladies who, through force of circumstances, have been compelled to work for their own living, none perhaps have made greater progress, and proved more beneficial to them, than that afforded by the United Telephone Company.

Originally this company employed male clerks in all its branches, but the idea presenting itself to the minds of the chairman and the directors that the work might easily be carried out by ladies, they decided upon a trial, with the determination to obtain the services of those whose birth and respectability, through reduced circumstances, rendered them suitable for employment.

After having mastered the necessary details required In the performance of the duties, I was appointed Lady Superintendent. We commenced work in the United Telephone Company's exchange at Westminster in September, 1880. Since then we have increased steadily, and at the present time nine of the Company exchanges are being worked by ladies, the staff now under my charge consisting of over one hundred assistants.

As an employment for ladies it has proved, therefore, not only a success as regards the work, but also as a channel for providing many of those employed with the means of supporting themselves entirely, whilst in the case of others it has not only been an advantage in a monetary sense of view, but at the same time has developed business-like habits and ideas, which are so essential to the progress of the work for women in the present day

I must add that every facility has been afforded me by the managing director of the company towards promoting the welfare of the young people who have come under my care; the exchanges having been altered and re-fitted with every improvement both to further the work and to insure the comfort of the employees, whilst the good conduct and cheerful perseverance in their duties has met with the entire satisfaction of the chairman and directors, and has been most encouraging to me in my efforts to make this work for ladies a success.

Louise Ellinor Merlin, Lady Superintendent, United Telephone Company, 36, Colman Street, E.C. April 8th, 1883

A group of 1911 operators. Back row (l-r): E Cowley, E M Tringham, J E Moore, Ada Buckwell, C Hooper, A H Smith, Ethel Epps. Second row: M Booth, B Wood, E Tringham, Beatrice Ashmead, M D Johnstone, A Willett, Constance Gregory, M Blakesley. Front row: A Reekie, Minnie F Butler, K Butcher, Constance Forge, E Richards, Edith Smith, Beatrice Newman, Ada Knapman. In front: L Stevens, Katherine Pring

To replace all the boy operators in London took some time. Miss Fanny Holmes was transferred in 1892 to Central Exchange, Oxford Court, when the boys were replaced by girls[6], and Miss Minnie Buttler was Clerk-in-Charge at London Wall exchange in 1898, at the time of the changeover from boy operators.[7]

The *Pall Mall Gazette*[8] describes the working of a London exchange in 1883.

"What, then, is a telephone exchange station? We will take the East India Avenue, in the City, as an average sample... in the attic is a room occupied by eleven young ladies. The 271 wires which represent the subscribers of the East India Avenue Exchange with 46 trunk and other direct wires, are guided down from the derrick above into neat mahogany cabinets or cases, in front of which the young ladies are seated. The alert dexterity with which the signal, given by the fall of a small lid about the size of a teaspoon, the lady hitches on the applicant to the number with which he desires to talk is pleasant to watch. On the day of our visit there had been in this one office no less than 2,400 calls. Here, indeed, is an occupation to which no 'heavy father' could object; and the result is a higher class of young woman can be obtained for the secluded career of a telephonist as compared with that which follows the more barmaid-like occupation of a telegraph clerk."

A girl starting work as an operator was given no formal training, but had to rely on one of the experienced operators teaching her as she went along, a method that was not always successful. Miss Constance Forge started as an operator in February, 1886, at Westminster; she recalls:

When I entered service and until comparatively recent years, there was no training school for operating and newcomers had to pick up what they could of the work from watching other operators. The latter were oft times far from tolerant in their treatment of these learners [9]

Miss Ralph, who eventually was given charge of an operating school for beginners in 1899 adds:

New operators were placed at the switchboard and told one or two necessary details of the work, and thus they started on their career. As to the names of the apparatus, Miss Ralph states she learnt only two, "indicators" and "pegs," the technical instruction of those days was very different from the elaborate and careful system she is now called upon to instil into recruits of the operating staff.[10]

Early exchanges were not known by name, they were allotted a group of numbers and when calls were made only the number was given by the subscriber, the operator having to remember the destination exchange from the number given. Miss Ralph again recalls:

When "learners" first entered the London service in those days they received a list of the exchanges showing the numbers allotted to each exchange; at that time there was only one set of numbers for the whole city and the names of the exchanges were not used in the subscribers list.

Miss Constance Gregory started as an operator in May, 1895, just before subscribers had to give the name of the exchange. She reported for duty at Colman Street, and, like all operators prior to August, 1899, was largely dependent on the good nature of those colleagues sitting on either side of her at the switchboard for her tuition. Her first duty was to learn the numbers of the different exchanges in London. Subscribers in asking for numbers, did not give in the name of the exchange, and the operators were therefore obliged to be perfectly acquainted with the divisions.[11]

Miss Butler continues:

When she started work for the United Telephone Company in June, 1883, at Cornhill, after presenting herself to the Clerk-in-Charge, she was given the usual list of exchanges showing the numbers allotted to each. When she had mastered these she was told a few details of the work and set to operate. Supervision was then unknown, operators were left entirely to their own resources and if anything out of the ordinary routine occurred they had to decide for themselves how best to deal with the matter.[12]

The allocation of numbers to exchanges,[13] for the most part remained constant, although, some changes were made when smaller exchanges were absorbed by larger units. This wouldn't have made the operator's job any easier. But as some of these mergers took place at the same time as the installation of new multiple switchboards the complexity of the new numbering would have been greatly reduced. Finally it was decided by the Metropolitan Superintendent, Mr Clay, in 1899 that in future a subscriber would have to give the exchange name as well as a number, putting an end to an unmanageable system.

The conditions under which operators worked in those early days were far from good. Miss Beatrice Ashmead, who was an operator at Hop exchange, then in the old Hop Market building, recollects the condition of things in connection with the so called dining and retiring room which only serves in common with others, who had the same experience, to make her more appreciative of the modern (1908) comforts provided.[14] Miss Newman, like all senior operating staff, has, in comparison with what they had to experience in the early days of their service, much to say in appreciation of the present arrangements for their comfort, and remembers, as a case in point, one exchange where the lunch-room was formed by dividing off a portion of the switchroom by a huge piece of baize provided with a sort of tent flap for entry and exit.

At Gerrard Exchange the operators were fortunate with their accommodation, their dining room featured a large ingle-nook fire place, a reminder of the days when it was the Pelican Club Members Room. From here a large open staircase swept up into the switchroom, that was once a billiard room large enough to contain six billiard tables[15].

Although operators worked hard, the same was not always the case with those who were in charge. Miss Holmes remembers how her Clerk-in-Charge at the old Queen Victoria exchange in 1888 spent her time reading and preparing her wedding trousseau.[16] The same thing apparently occurred at Hop exchange where Miss Knapman saw her Clerk-in-Charge engaged in fancy work. This particular lady, who shortly left to get married, made nearly the whole of her trousseau in the exchange.[17]

With regards to meals, the company did not provide any facilities. Miss Ralph:

Each operator was allowed one shilling [5p] weekly in addition to her salary for tea, but as no lunching arrangements existed the girls brought their own food and cooked it over an open fire in the exchange.[18]

Miss Edith Smith:
In those days there was apparently no scale of pay and increases were conspicuous by their absence. When the Edison switchboard at Queen Victoria Street was changed over to a multiple type, the receipt of a bonus by each operator on this occasion was hailed with delight. [19]

The United Telephone Company provided their engineers with an all round training, by giving them practical experience at all the various operations connected with running the telephone system. Shortly after leaving school William Cook began his telephone career with the United Telephone Company in May, 1884. His earliest practical work. was "curling" cables, (curling cables, would have been forming out wires to the switchboard jacks and then lacing them into position) for the first multiple switchboard in London at Chancery Lane exchange. When he had completed this job, he was transferred to the Fault Department, which at that time had its head-quarters at Oxford Court and operated over the central metro-politan area. It was no uncommon thing to be sent from the East End to the West End of London to attend two consecutive faults. Mr Cook was then sent to work as an operator at the Central Trunk Exchange in Oxford Court. After a few months practical experience at the switchboard, he was transferred to the exchange electrical staff, which carried out the construction and maintenance work in connection with the London exchanges.[20]

John Hidden, who started with the electrical staff of the United Telephone Company at Oxford Court in 1886, recalled:

In these early days of telephone development the work was particularly interesting, covering as it did all branches of electrical work the switchboards and apparatus were of a very varied nature, consisting of Bell slipper pattern boards, Edison peg boards, flat slipper pattern boards on the multiple system (Hawes) and branching jack multiple boards (Western Electric). The maintenance staff were very much dependent upon their own resources in clearing trouble on the switchboards. It seems a far cry in these days of common battery boards [written in 1910], when a portable testing set is provided which will locate about twenty different kinds of faults by merely pressing a button or putting over a lever, back in those days when to clear a fault on the Edison peg board an inspector carried a screwdriver, galvanometer and a piece of stiff notepaper The faults were generally "earths" or contacts between the brass strips caused by brass filings.[21]

Reginald Dalzell joined the Globe Telephone Company in 1881 as an exchange fitter; here he recalls:

The first work assigned to him, was that of fitting two sections of an upright multiple board, in the switchroom which was for a short time in operation at the Wool Exchange the method adopted by the American engineer-in-charge was of fitting the sections back to back with a working space between. Wires passed from one to the other under the flooring.

This, of course, was against all the principles of multiple working: the boards should have been side by side as Mr Dalzell points out 'proving that the value of the multiple was hardly understood'. Later, when the United Telephone Company took over the Globe, Mr Dalzell took a position on their staff.[22]

How was the telephone viewed by the subscriber? Unfortunately there were complaints about the service, but in the main business was brisk for those who accepted the telephone into their establishments. As the following extract from the *Norwich Argus* of 1885[23]:
In due course we found ourselves at our trysting-place, Haxwell's

Hotel, in West Strand. We were shown our apartments; and descending again, we were amused to watch the ever-coming applicants at the Telephone Office in the hall of the hotel. The hotel clerk has possession of the instrument. "Who speaks?" came distinctly from the wires into the office. "2577," was the reply - it was the hotel number. "Put me into communication with 1200." "What is it?" was the instantaneous rejoinder. "Can we have two stalls for the Princess's; two stalls, Covent Garden; three stalls, Criterion; two stalls, St James's; all for tonight. Private box, Lyceum to-morrow; three stalls, Haymarket, Saturday; and four dress-circles, Drury-Lane, morning performance, Monday?" With scarcely a minute's delay there came clearly along the wire, "All reserved; numbers sent up this morning, with Mr Hayes' compliments." And oddly enough during the whole of this colloquy, I could hear the music of *La Traviata*, which someone was brilliantly running through in the office, over one mile away in the City. We then rang up "3501" (Messrs. Thornhill, of Bond Street). "Are any of the firm at home?" "No; they are at the Sportsman's Show, Agricultural Hall, but you can 'get through' to them as we have the wire laid on to our exhibit there." In a few minutes we were "through!" and, to reply to our inquiry, heard Mr Barker's voice clear and distinct, as if he had been at our elbow, instead of at a distance of about four miles! A few minutes later, and the hotel cellar man came up to beg pardon. "Sir," said he "We have had a run upon minerals, and are nearly out." "Come," said Haxwell to me, "you shall have another proof of the value of this little fellow." Again was the tiny bell put in motion "2577 wishes to speak with H D Rawlings." "Is that you, dear old man?" "Yes, dear old boy. We are out of minerals. Kindly send us as soon as possible one gross of seltzer, one gross of soda, one gross of lemon, and half that quantity of splits all round." We had scarcely left the office when once more the little bell sent forth its shrill peal." "Who speaks?" said the clerk. "2536, Wood's Hotel, Holborn. We have just sent you two gentleman who wish to be close to Charing Cross, and Mr Whaley desires me to say that he is pleased to make as prompt a return for those you sent us last week." "It is really a great convenience and profit," we said to Haxwell. "Why," said he, "and so we find it. But think of the advantage it will be when I shall be enabled, through the introduction of it into Brighton, to hold instant communication with my manager of my hotel there." And so we parted, for I had business in the City; and this is my one hour's experience at the

Telephone Office at Haxwell's Hotel, London.

1 *The Electrician* 31st July, 1880
2 *NTJ* July, 1907 p 75.
3 *NTJ* June, 1908 p 52.
4 *NTJ* Sept, 1909 p 111 .
5 *NTJ* Nov, 1911 p 158.
6 *NTJ* Jan, 1910 p 207.
7 *NTJ* July, 1911 p 72.
8 *Pallmall Gazette*, 6th Dec 1883.
9 *NTJ* July, 1909 p 232.
10 *NTJ* July, 1907 p 75.
11 *NTJ* April, 1911 p 9.
12 *NTJ* July, 1911 p 72.
13 List Given In Appendix.
14 *NTJ* Nov, 1908 p 174.
15 *The Building News* 5th July, 1889.
16 *NTJ* Jan, 1910 p 207.
17 *NTJ* Nov, 1908 p 174.
18 *NTJ* July, 1907 p 75.
19 *NTJ* Feb, 1908.
20 *NTJ* Aug, 1908.
21 *NTJ* Feb, 1910.
22 *NTJ* April, 1908.
23 United Telephone Company Directory, 1885.
Reprinted as *Three Victorian Telephone Directories*. David & Charles.

Holborn Exchange in roof of Birkbeck Bank Buildings, 1904

THE NATIONAL TELEPHONE COMPANY IN LONDON

In May, 1889, the United Telephone Company merged with The National Telephone Company and the Lancashire and Cheshire Telephonic Exchange Company, in an effort to consolidate and bring some uniformity to an ever expanding telephone system. The new company was called The National Telephone Company as this was the name of the largest of the three at the time of the merger.

Prior to January, 1905, the London telephone system was managed on more or less the same lines as those in the provinces. London was divided into six districts, City, West, South, East, North, and Croydon, each with a District Manager and separate staff. The City District manager's office was at 58-59 London Wall and was responsible for Avenue, Bank and Holborn exchanges. The Eastern District office was situated in Grove Road, Stratford, and consisted of three small rooms over a boot shop, and controlled Eastern, Stratford and Tilbury exchanges. By 1895 the Western District manager had offices In the Pelican Club building, along with Gerrard exchange and was responsible for Gerrard, Westminster, Kilburn, Kensington, Paddington, Harrow, Harlesden,

Hammersmith and Ealing. The southern district had its head-quarters at 6-8 Marshalsea Road, and controlled Hop, Deptford, Battersea, Clapton, Peckham, Woolwich and other exchanges south of the river. The Northern District office was at Colvestone House, Ridley Road, Dalston, and amongst other exchanges controlled King's Cross and Holloway. Lastly, Croydon district office was at 71 Church Street. In January, 1905, the London Centralization Scheme was introduced by the National Telephone Company. All London staff were merged and the District Manager posts were abolished and replaced with a central administration from offices taken by the company in December, 1904, at Salisbury House, 57 London Wall. The National Telephone Company's national head office remained at Oxford Court, Cannon Street, until 1901, when it was moved into a new building at Temple Place, just off the Victoria Embankment, called Telephone House.

Much of the exchange equipment, line plant, and telephones inherited by the National Telephone Company in London was inadequate and antiquated for the demands being made upon it by the growth of the system. Between the late 1880's and the early 1890's, the National Telephone Company began to replace the earlier D.C. trembler bells in telephone instruments with A.C. magneto bells. These were superior to the old type and were very reliable, needing less critical adjustments. At the same time telephone instruments were provided with a small hand generator to call the exchange. The chairman reported to the National Telephone Company's Annual General Meeting in July, 1890,[1] that 1700 battery bells of the old sort were replaced with magneto sets, there remained 350 still to be changed. The shareholders present were also told of the recent replacement of earlier slipper jack and Edison switchboards with multiple boards. Only two remained to be renewed, although not named, they were probably Hop and Heddon Street. Even after this work was carried, out it soon became clear, that a complete overhaul of switching equipment, and the re-location, and eventual rebuilding, of exchanges would be necessary to provide expansion of the service in the future. The search for suitable buildings to house telephone exchanges was a difficult task in such a densely built up area as the City and West End of London. Although a number of suitable buildings were found it was evidently not a satisfactory way of providing accommodation in the future. So in 1897 the National Telephone Company, adopted a national policy of providing purpose built exchanges, designed for immediate switching capacity and expansion when required.

From 1893 the National Telephone Company tried to bring some standardisation to their exchange switchboards. At the same time there was a great debate between leading Telephone Engineers of the day, on the rival merits of the horizontal multiple, or the vertical multiple, being adopted for large manual exchange switchboards of the future. The deciding factor for the National Telephone Company was economic, as the patent for the vertical multiple was held by the Western Electric Company and the cost of the equipment was considerable. The horizontal board provided a means of reducing these costs, the multiple was available at each position to two operators, one on each side of the board, very similar to sitting each side of a table. There was of course serious disadvantages, least of which was the need for some operators to work on a multiple where the number, appeared upside down. The cost of cabling was greater and access for maintenance could only be given when the board was not busy. Even so a number of these boards were installed in central London exchanges.

By 1892 the Western Electric Company had introduced into commercial service a switchboard which they termed A Self Restoring Indicator Branching Multiple board. The advantages of this development in switchboard design were soon appreciated by telephone companies. The 'Self Restoring Indicators', meant that it was no longer necessary for the subscriber's calling indicators to be in reach of the operator, who previously had to restore the indicator flaps to their latched position by hand. These indicators could now be moved from their previous position in the area of the key shelf, to the top of the board above the operator's head. Another advantage was the 'Branching Multiple', this term described the way the Jacks were wired, on earlier boards these had been wired in series, looped from one jack to the next. If the contacts became dirty or the springs became 'light tensioned,' subsequent jacks after the faulty one would become useless. The new method was to wire break jacks in parallel so only the faulty jack was out of service, the wiring was 'branched' into each jack from a continuous stem. These boards were provided in sections and could be added to as the requirements of the exchange grew. The Self Restoring Indicator Branching Multiple was ideally suited for the horizontal switchboard, although the boards used in London were of a slightly different design to those elsewhere in the country. They were a hybrid of the vertical and horizontal multiple switchboards of the Self Restoring Indicator Branching System. The calling and clearing indicators were on the face of the overhead canopy. Both calling and answering cords were on the key shelf, the vertical between the keys and the horizontal multiple contained the subscriber's answering jacks and the outgoing junction jacks for connecting calls to other exchanges. This system only worked where a majority of calls were for other exchanges and local calls on the same exchange were at a minimum, as the calling cords lay across the horizontal multiple when a local call was connected. Incoming calls from other exchanges were connected by cords pulled down from the canopy and plugged straight into the multiple below.

In the next phase of switchboard development all the electrical power required for the operation of the telephone system was concentrated in the exchange. The London Globe Telephone and Maintenance Company's Telephone System in 1882, was developed by A L Anders, and was unique in having a common battery for signalling, and another common battery for speech between two connected subscribers. This took away the necessity of providing each subscriber's instrument with a separate battery and the considerable cost of maintaining them. Some ten years passed before the concept of central, or common battery was again experimented with in America. By 1898 a single voltage common battery system was established. Two other developments that coincided with the common battery was the improvement in relays, the hinge portion or armature being pivoted on a 'knife edge.' It also became possible to produce small and very efficient electric lamps, which were able to work with higher voltages. In 1889 the Western Electric Company installed an experimental demonstration

Old Gerrard Exchange, at one time the Pelican Club

Central or Common Battery exchange at their Woolwich works followed by the first central battery exchange at Bristol, opened for service in April, 1900, by the National Telephone Company.

The advantages of the Common Battery system over its forerunners were many, but the most important was the use of electric lamps for signalling. This was a great advance over the drop flap indicator. It was more compact, attracted the operator's attention more effectively and, above all, was silent. The more complex working parts, such as relays, could be located away from the switchboard in a more accessible position. The transmission quality of the circuit was improved as the central battery was charged by motor generators driven from the public electricity supply, thus ensuring uniform line voltage. The subscriber's telephone apparatus was also simplified with the removal of the battery and the magneto generator. After a few minor improvements the No 1 C.B. exchange was provided by the National Telephone Company as a standard replacement for updating earlier municipal exchanges throughout the country and was the ultimate in manual telephony. Some of the largest changeovers ever attempted took place at this time, needing remarkably detailed planning and testing, with an almost military precision. Disconnecting thousands of circuits from existing equipment and re-connecting service on the new, in a matter of a few minutes. The operation of the C.B. switchboard was comparatively simple after its predecessors, and has been described by Mr Hall Ellis[2]:

When a subscriber wishes to make a call, all he need do is lift his receiver. This completes his line circuit, through which a current now flows from the exchange battery. The exchange battery provides current for his transmitter. At the exchange a relay is operated which causes a small lamp to light on the switchboard. To answer the call, the operator uses a cord circuit as in the magneto system, but in the C.B. system the answering jack is adjacent to the calling lamp, and the cords are conveniently placed on the key shelf.

As before, the operator connects to the required number in the multiple. In line with each cord circuit two small supervisory lamps are provided on the key shelf, and these light up when the calling and called subscribers respectively hang up at the end of the call. This largely obviates any need for the operator to enter the circuit to supervise a call.

1 *The Electrician*, July, 1890.
2 Hall Ellis, *The Early years of the Telephone Service in Bristol*.

NATIONAL TELEPHONE COMPANY EXCHANGES IN LONDON

Five years after the formation of the National Telephone Company, it became clear that a number of the larger London exchanges would need to move to more commodious premises if they were to continue in those areas of London where they operated. These moves were made between late 1894 and early 1896.

Avenue exchange was moved to new premises previously occupied by the Hudson Bay Company on the top floor at 2 Lime Street. They were acquired by the National Telephone Company in September, 1890. Mr Cook, National Telephone Company's London Electrician,[1] was given the job of drawing up the specification for the switchboard, which was a Western Electric Company Self restoring Indicator Branching System with upright Multiple. The first of these boards. were installed in Hull and opened in 1893. The Avenue exchange should have been the first to open, but difficulties in completing the external work delayed the opening until 7th August, 1894.

Edgware Road Exchange was also modernised at this period by the National Telephone Company. Miss Smith,[2] who was Clerk in Charge between 1890 and 1892 recalled the change over from transfer (slipper jack) to multiple working, she gives the impression that the multiple board was installed at 77 Market Street (re-named St Michael's Street in 1938). The street directory refers to 77 Market Street as occupied by the Dudley Stuart Home for training young girls for domestic service until 1895 and does not list the National Telephone Company as occupiers until 1896-1897. Taking this into account it was possible that the new board was installed at this later date, and was most likely to have been an Upright Branching Multiple similar to that at Avenue. At the same time the exchange became known as Paddington.

Modernisation also took place at Westminster where Ada Buckwell recalled that a new switchboard was fitted in February, 1896[3]. Again there is no record of the type so it must be assumed that it was similar to Avenue. Ada Buckwell was promoted to Clerk in Charge at Westminster in 1907. During this period the exchange was enlarged, having some 1,500 subscribers. In the National Telephone Company Building Records, there is an entry: 14 Victoria Street, 3rd and 4th floors, 24th June, 1902, Exchange. I have been unable to establish any facts about the entry. It is possible that the new board of 1896 was situated at this address, or that the National Telephone Company acquired the property ready to install a new C.B. No 1 switchboard, an improvement that never took place as Westminster remained a magneto exchange until the demise of the Company. Of course, the re-numbering of Victoria Street between 1889 and 1890 cannot be overlooked. From the street directories, it appears that some businesses previously at No 6 were re-numbered No 10 and those of No 4 became No 14. There is thus a possibility that the exchange previously referred to as No 6, and that at No 14 were the same.

On 29th September, 1891, the National Telephone Company acquired premises at 58-59 London Wall, opposite the London headquarters of the National Telephone Company at Salisbury House, 57 London Wall. Here, the National Telephone Company opened an exc:hange to replace the old Wool Exchange. The exact date is not known, but some clues do exist. The *National Telephone Company Journal*, April, 1911, tells us that Miss Constance Gregory started work as an operator at Coleman Street in 1895. The exchange had by then already moved to the Wool Exchange but continued to be known as Coleman Street[4]. There is another reference in the *Journal*, July, 1911, that Miss Minnie Butler was made Clerk in Charge of London Wall in 1898, so the move from the Wool Exchange to London Wall would have taken place

between these two dates. I suspect that 1896 would have been the time, as a number of other exchanges were modernised at this period and although no record of the type of switchboard exists, I expect it was one of the Western Electric Upright Branching Multiples.

Chancery Lane exchange became absorbed by a new exchange, which was opened at Holborn in St Andrews Street, just off Holborn Circus in August, 1894. Here, a Self Restoring Indicator Branching System with Horizontal Multiple, was installed, incidentally the first of this type in London. This was soon followed by the renewal of the old Queen Victoria exchange in Victoria Street, which at the same time moved into new premises at 31 Queen Victoria Street. These were originally the offices of The Globe Telephone Company, where a new horizontal multiple switchboard was opened in December, 1894, and became known as Bank Exchange.

The Heddon Street exchange was now proving to be too small for further expansion, so Mr Moorhouse, who was Assistant Engineer for the West End was instructed to look for vacant premises in the neighbourhood for a new exchange. He eventually brought the company's attention to the old Pelican Club, in Gerrard Street. This was at first thought too large for their purpose, but it was eventually purchased and a horizontal multiple switchboard was installed in early 1895[5]. In the summer of 1897 the horizontal switchboard in Gerrard, now the new name for Heddon Street, needed an overhaul and a partial rewire along with a new power plant. This was undertaken by a special staff who worked entirely at night all through the summer of 1897. Mr Cohen, a switchboard fitter at the time, remembers that it was strenuous; sometimes it was necessary to work continuously from a Saturday evening until Monday morning [6].

Over in South London, the Hop Market exchange was closed in 1895 and a horizontal multiple switchboard installed in new premises at 6-8 Marshalsea Road, acquired in September, 1893. Miss Beatrice Newman, who was Clerk in Charge at the time, recalled the dread that these changeovers were viewed with[7]. It must be remembered that previous change-overs had only affected a hundred or so subscribers and were carried out in the same building, so could be completed over a period of time. As some of these latest change-overs were also combined with a change of address not only was it necessary to cut over the exchange in one go, but it was also necessary to do a large amount of preliminary work teeing in cables and wires to the new exchange building. Also the operators not only had to be prepared to work the new style switchboards, but become used to a different multiple layout within minutes of the changeover.

Whether the horizontal switchboards, at Holborn and Hop, were eventually recovered and replaced by a vertical magneto board, or whether they lasted until the change over to the C.B. No 1 is not known. The horizontal board at Gerrard Street was replaced. George Greenham was exchange inspector and took part in the installation of the 'Christina' board between 1897 and 1899. Why this board received this name is unclear, except that Kingsbury in *The telephone and telephone exchanges* states that the capital of Norway (Christina), was the first place in Europe to have a Western Electric Self Restoring Indicator Branching Multiple switchboard installed.

1 *NTJ*, Aug, 1908.
2 *NTJ*, Feb, 1908.
3 *NTJ*, July, 1911 p 72.
4 See Telephone Directories, Sep, 1889
5 *NTJ*, June, 1911.
6 *NTJ*, Oct, 1911.
7 *NTJ*, Nov, 1907

THE CENTRAL BATTERY
EXCHANGES
OF THE
NATIONAL TELEPHONE
COMPANY IN LONDON

Between 1901 and 1908, the National Telephone Company, replaced all their central London magneto exchanges with new central battery No I systems. Some of the old exchange buildings were completely demolished and replaced by new buildings of the latest design, incorporating switchrooms on the top floor, with ancillary equipment, staff accommodation and offices on the lower floors The necessary changeovers from magneto to C.B. working involved a great deal of careful and meticulous planning for it not only involved a changeover of a large number of circuits with the very minimum of interruption but a completely new way of working for the operators and a change of operation for the subscribers. The first of these Common Battery exchanges to be installed in London was opened in Kensington on 21st December, 1901, at 52 Sussex Place (now Launceston Place).

Kensington was followed on the 1st March, 1902, by the opening of a C.B. No I exchange at 58-59 London Wall. Due to the difficulty of finding a spacious site in this part of London, this exchange was

of unusual construction. The switchboard stood on long cast iron galleries that ran the length and to one side of the building, one above the other. On the evening of 9th July, 1902, a disastrous fire started at eight o'clock in the evening and by ten thirty the whole exchange had been gutted[1]. The fire had been intensified by the melting of paraffin wax that surrounded the cables that ran from floor to floor. These cable risers were apparently an object of pride, being kept highly polished. After the fire the

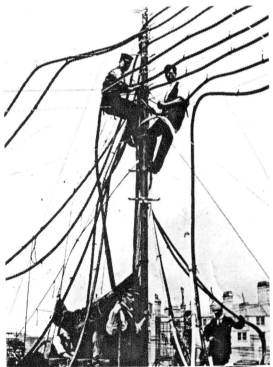

Overhead cable gang diverting cables after the fire at London Wall Exchange, 1902

Birkbeck Bank, Southampton Buildings, in 1903. Holborn Exchange was installed in the upper storeys in 1904

engineering and instrument departments, which occupied the adjoining building (59 London Wall) were vacated into other premises. Then switchboards along with other material, stored at the Nottingham factory for such emergencies as this, were requisitioned by telephone and dispatched by rail in trucks attached to passenger trains. This apparatus arrived at London Wall the next day Mr Clay, the metropolitan superintendent, put together a work force of expert exchange fitters, jointers and other skilled workmen from London, and other parts of the country. They were divided into day and night gangs, fitting up the temporary switchboards and joining up the overhead cables. They worked continuously and a large number of subscribers were re-connected each day. The complete restoration of some 2,600 subscribers took 16 days[2]. The job included erecting one hundred new outside cables with three double and six single poles to carry the cables and in two cases piers had to be built and girders put in to support the poles. More than 420 miles of outside wire and 334 miles of inside wire had to be run and although the exchange was a temporary one it gave a thoroughly good and efficient service. The rebuilding of London Wall exchange went ahead and the installation of new C.B. No I equipment and switchboards was

nearly completed at the end of January 1905[3]. Although another month of testing had been planned, a second fire took place in the roof top test room of the temporary exchange next door.

Although it was discovered almost immediately, the test room was destroyed and water badly damaged the cables and other apparatus. As the new exchange was almost ready the whole of the old exchange, consisting of some 3,800 subscribers, 1,000 junctions along with another 1,000 miscellaneous circuits, was transferred to the new exchange ready for operation the next morning on the 28th of January at 9.40 a m. The cause of the fires was never discovered.

In 1903 estimates were prepared for the replacement of most of the larger magneto exchanges in London by common battery equipment. The first exchange to be dealt with under this plan was, Holborn. The existing Holborn exchange was transferred from St Andrews Street to new premises at 329 High Holborn where a C.B. No I was installed in the upper stories of the Birkbeck Bank Building opening on the 14th of May, 1904, with Miss Edith Smith as Clerk-in-Charge.

The new C.B. No I at Hop exchange was opened for service on 17th March, 1906, at 9 Marshalsea Road, in premises opposite

London Wall Exchange after the 1905 fire. Engineers diverting the cables

the old magneto exchange. The switchboards were arranged on two floors and access for running the cables between the two exchanges prior to the changeover was by a subway under the road. Beatrice Newman who was Clerk in Charge at the time of the transfer already had previous experience, having been in charge when Hop was transferred from the Market building to 6-8 Marshalsea Road[4]. Her supervisors and operators were re-trained to work the C.B. No.1 equipment, using a full sized chart of the new switchboard showing the position of the new lamp cap codes. After this, practice was obtained by operating staff working at other exchanges. The usual military style precision that always accompanied these large exchange changeovers was recorded in the *National Telephone Journal*[5]:

On the date of opening at 2.30 pm word was given to the Maintenance Department that all was ready. Half the junctions were then thrown out of use at the old exchange while the traffic was worked on the second half. The preliminary junctions having been proved with less than the number of faults anticipated, the word was passed by the official controlling the changeover to cut in the subscribers. The signal was immediately given to the clerk-in-charge at the old exchange, and half the operators left the old exchange, with their new instruments adjusted, and filed in an orderly manner across the road. On reaching the new switch room each operator walked to the position previously assigned to her, and stood behind her chair. At a given signal the operators plugged into their positions and took their seats; simultaneously the little green lamp of the instruction circuit glowed and the word passed to release the relays, by plugging into the answering jacks with a switch board plug. Immediately each operator became busy. Meanwhile the second section of operators was called and, as previously instructed, tested the calling lamps by a short circuit plug, while the inspectors were kept busy proving the remainder of the junctions.

This changeover must have caused quite a spectacle at the time. Perhaps a policeman held up the traffic while the procession crossed the road, we will never know. Full credit was given to Miss Beatrice Newman, a strict disciplinarian, but one has only to know her thoroughly to appreciated the conscientiousness which governs every detail of her work, without doubt her organising ability and imperturbable coolness went far to bring about the ease with which the operators took up the working of the new switchboard after the change over from magneto to central battery system at the Hop

Exchange[6].

The next exchange to be modernised was Eastern. The original exchange in the Eastern Hotel attic had been transferred to equipment supplied from the defunct Globe Company. This was in all probability installed at 14, West India Dock Road. In 1901 the National Telephone Company acquired numbers 15 (Broughton Williams), 17, (Julian Joseph boarding house) and 19, (Abraham Benjamin builder).These premises were bounded on one side by a seamen's hostel called Strangers Home for Asiatic, Africans and Southsea Islanders, and on the other by Rugg Street and Blundell's London Copper and Brass Works. Into these three properties the Company moved its Eastern District Offices. There is also evidence to suggest that one of these properties housed a magneto exchange replacing that at number 14. Anyway, by 1906, 15, 17 and 19 were demolished and a purpose-built exchange had been erected, and on 26th May, 1906, a new C.B. No I exchange was opened. With the opening of the new Eastern Exchange, a centralisation scheme under the direction of Mr. Moorhouse took place. The Albert Dock Exchange was closed and, along with a considerable portion of the Stratford subscribers, was transferred to the new exchange. Practically all the overhead wires in East London were replaced with an underground system at about the same time.

With increased demands for the telephone in the West End, the National Telephone Company soon found they were unable to expand Gerrard exchange any further in the old Pelican Club building. The only answer would be to erect a purpose built exchange with switchboards,

The new Gerrard Exchange being built alongside the old Pelican Club

National Telephone Company Gerrard Exchange Building, 1907, designed by Leonard Stokes

office and staff accommodation, so the adjoining properties 32 & 33 Gerrard Street and 8, 9 & 10 Lisle Street were bought, thus giving a large 'L' shaped site.

The design for the new building was given to Leonard Stokes (1858-1925), who in 1898 had married Edith Gaine, daughter of the General Manager of the National Telephone Company. Out of 19 exchanges designed by Stokes, Gerrard was his best known[7]. The building was begun in 1904 on the site of the demolished property adjoining the Pelican Club building and was so arranged that completion of the new building could take place in two stages, thus accommodating the inevitable change over from 'old' to 'new' equipment..

The new exchange was opened on 28th September, 1907, amid a plethora of newspaper reports. The old Pelican Club exchange, of which it is said that the post holes of a boxing ring could still be seen in the basement, was then demolished. The sign of the Pelican with three chicks that topped the building frontage, was given to a member of the staff.

The new building was then extended to cover the whole site with switchrooms on the top floor under the roof and commodious operators' rest room and dining room on the first floor, while company offices for electrician and line staff were situated on the ground floor. Gerrard became the prestige building of the National Telephone Company in London. Pictures of the exchange were used by many publications of the period, which ran articles on telephony. The transfer of Gerrard was the largest of its kind in London, with no fewer than 12,000 working circuits. The whole changeover took place in approximately 14 minutes, with a hundred or so operators marching from the old building into the new, where the new board, consisting of 105 'A' positions and 48 'B' positions, was situated. These 153 positions gave a 10,400 line capacity and used 26,000 signalling lamps, room being provided for a further 10,000 lines, for future exchange growth.

It is interesting to note that 150 operators in this exchange handled about 195,600 calls manually every day.

July, 1906, saw the partly completed rebuilding of Paddington exchange. The property adjoining 77 Market Street and that backing on to the old exchange in Star Street, had been bought up and demolished. The new building was started on the east side of the old exchange and when it was completed the old building was demolished and the new building extended. The 140ft frontage was of stock brick with stone dressings and bands of red brick. During the construction of the new exchange the builders had to contend with the old exchange derrick, two poles of which were on the outside of the new building, while the other two poles were on the inside and in the line of a new roof strut. These poles were lifted to a new position and the arms were re-arranged to allow for the new roof strut to be inserted. The new building was of four floors, ground floor offices; first floor operators quarters; second floor termination of subscribers' connections and power plant and the third floor, under a barrel shaped roof, the switchroom. The new exchange was opened to traffic on 9th March, 1907. There was a delay in the delivery of stores to complete the job, and a mysterious fault on the junction circuits was only cleared, by a modification, completed the day before the change over took place. The old building could now be demolished and the new one finally completed.[8]

1 *NTJ* Jan, 1912 p 216
2 *NTJ* Nov, 1906 p 156
3 *NTJ* Nov, 1906 p 164
4 *NTJ* Nov, 1907 p 160
5 *NTJ* Aug, 1906 p 104
6 *NTJ* Nov, 1907 p 161
7 *Edwardian Architecture and its origins*. Alastair Service. The Architectural Press
8 *NTJ* July, 1906 p 75

Gerrard Exchange. Miss Richards, Clerk in Charge, sitting centre back. Metropolitan Electrician, George Greenham, on left

OVERHEAD TELEPHONE WIRES IN LONDON UNDER THE NATIONAL TELEPHONE COMPANY

Like its predecessors, the National Telephone Company was unable to negotiate with the London authorities, now the London County Council, underground routes for their wires and cables in central London. In consequence providing and maintaining the required overhead network of wires, cables, poles and standards was a mammoth task. In fact, many of the old shackle insulators that had been in use since the early days of the telephone were only just being replaced in 1890, with the more modern pattern which we still see occasionally today. To add to this already formidable array of overhead lines two further issues had to be addressed. The National Telephone Company had to comply with the London Overhead Wire Act, passed by Parliament in 1891. This Act provided for the regulation of overhead telegraph and telephone wires. All new wires had to be erected in accordance with by-laws and existing wires removed if they were considered a danger to the public. There were a number of obligations under the Act, not the least of which was to provide full particulars of the material and

Overhead cables and roof standard in Dean Street

gauge of existing wires, the length of span, type of support, and also the line of route. As already noted, early telephones in London were worked on an earth return system. Unfortunately, as electricity began to be used more extensively for other services that also used earth return, such as trams, telephone transmission began to grow increasingly more noisy almost to the point of being inaudible. This forced the National Telephone Company to act, so in the October of 1892 the metallic circuiting of telephone lines in London began. To

The largest exchange derrick in London at Avenue Exchange, 1907

carry this out, each subscriber's line was provided with a second conductor between the telephone and the exchange. The task was enormous and very expensive. It needed an outlay of capital that it would be impossible to recover and was not completed until 1898. During this time of transition between the two systems, modifications needed to be made to accommodate both earth return and metallic circuits on the switchboard. Although no references to London switchboards having dual working have been found, I am sure that this must have been the case considering the time taken to convert the system.

For us today to try and envisage the unique conditions that engineers encountered in that aerial world working up above the City streets is practically impossible and can only now be captured by the descriptions published by Francis G C Baldwin who was, from 1910, Acting Metropolitan Engineer for the National Telephone Company with responsibility for the whole of the external line plant in London:
No one without practical experience

1905 fire at Bank Exchange. Man in bowler hat (r) is P T Wood, electrician. 3rd from right, Foreman Bullimore

can possibly appreciate the immensity of the work involved in giving service to large numbers of subscribers, situated within the confines of the City of London, by overhead means. A visit by the uninitiated to the roofs of the City of London when the telephone service was administered by the National Telephone Company would, doubtless, have been a matter of considerable interest. On many of the roofs of these high buildings one might walk without impediment for considerable distances, crossing from one building to another either direct, or by means of gangways specially provided for the purpose. A peculiar quiet reigned in spite of the noise of traffic in the busy streets below. One seemed translated from the world of the London streets to quite a different and remote world - seemingly without any relation to the London of common conception. In all directions amidst chimney stacks, ventilators, water tanks, and other appurtenances, radiate innumerable wires and cables of various sizes, supported on huge derricks, roof poles and standards, with their numerous stays, the whole inanimate without apparent purpose, yet constituting the main medium by which the citizens of London conduct their communic- ations. This realm of wire, both insulated and bare, was as well known, or even better than the streets below, to the men who lived their daily lives within it, attending to its peculiar needs, extending it or adding to or subtracting from it as occasion demanded.

It must be mentioned here that the derrick on the roof of Avenue Exchange in Lime Street was the largest in London. A massive octagonal structure, on which some 12,000 wires were terminated and built on a purposely strengthened roof. To achieve maximum flexibility in the London telephone system, junction or cross connection boxes were provided at strategic points, some 500 or so of these existed in the city alone. They were mounted in accessible areas, against a convenient wall or at the bottom of a pole or standard. One of the largest of these distribution centres was situated on the roof of 31 Throgmorton Street, the four iron uprights of the derrick structure enclosed a hut in which were terminated 62 aerial cables containing some 3,258 circuits. This hut had an almost continual attendance by engineers to deal with the constant flow of new connections, removals, alterations and general testing, in fact it was an exchange test room in miniature. Baldwin continues:

This distributing system, although unsatisfactory from many points of view, no telephone engineer would have objected to its wholesale demolition following its replacement by a modern underground system, possessed certain advantages: its arrangement was such that a high degree of flexibility was attained, and so long as serious disturbance

Working on overhead cables at Holborn, c.1900

due to wayleave or other trouble did not arise, alterations could be made with commendable rapidity.

An operation which frequently attracted a good deal of public interest in the streets of London was one pertaining to the maintenance of the numerous aerial cables, namely, that of the renewal of the No 10 S.W.G. galvanised steel wires from which the cables were suspended by means of raw hide slings: the number of such wires used for one cable was proportional according to the weight of the cable to be supported and to the length of the span. These steel wires had an effective life, in London, of something of the order of seven years, and it was therefore no infrequent occurrence

Renewing aerial cable suspenders in mid-air over London, 1909

for the operation of renewal to be witnessed. That part of the work that aroused wonderment and sometimes the concern of the public consisted of the transfer of a cable from the old to a new set of suspending wires erected for the purpose, by workman suspended from the new wires in a bosun's chair. The position of the man dangling at such a height over mid street from a wire of such comparatively slender proportions has the appearance of being a hazardous one, but owing to the precautions taken, the danger is perhaps no greater than that to pedestrians exposed to the risks of traffic in the streets below.

Derrick and test hut at 31 Throgmorton Street

65

As with the United Telephone Company, the two worst enemies of this overhead network were fire and snow. Winters were looked on with apprehension as the snow fell on the cables and wires, increasing their weight until they literally tore the poles and fixings from their roof top perches. After a particularly nasty snow storm in February, 1891, a subscriber wrote to *The Times*:

'May we be allowed to mention that most of the instruments in South Audley Street, including our own, have been rendered useless since the snow storm which occurred the week before last. Nor, in reply to enquiries at the district exchange as recently as this afternoon, have we been able to obtain more than a general assurance that the communication will be restored as speedily as possible!'

Fire was also a great danger to overhead plant due to the inflammable nature of the insulation used on aerial cables and wires. When a fire was reported the London Fire Brigade notified the telephone company, so that engineers could take the necessary precautions to prevent the fire spreading from one building to another. Gangs of workmen were often sent up aloft in the heat and smoke to cut down burning cables from near by buildings. In June, 1898, considerable damage was done by a fire in Heddon Street. *The Times* reported:

The fire in Heddon Street, Regent Street, which was briefly mentioned in a portion of our impression of yesterday, broke out at 1-15 yesterday morning in a large building tenanted by Messrs Davies, Kent and Stewart, and several other firms. Commander Wells, R.N., assisted by Superintendent T Smith, set 19 steamers [fire engines] to work. The morning had far advanced however before the brigade could overcome the fire. The firemen had to complain of a short supply of water in the early minutes of the fire. A huge telephone stand on the top of the burning building suddenly collapsed and the mass of metal weighing some forty tons, crashed into the centre of a body of firemen at the front of Superintendent Smith, in its fall it smashed the long ladder, but no fireman was injured .[1]

With such a high density of overhead cables. and wires running over the roof tops any building that caught fire caused havoc with the telephone system. On 12th September, 1906[2], a fire at 47 - 48 Holborn Viaduct caused much damage to a double standard, (two telephone poles connected by their cross-arms) which was fixed to the party wall of the buildings. The damage left 341 exchange lines, 59 private circuits and 140 junctions between Holborn, Bank and London

Holborn Exchange derrick. Possibly at St Andrews Street

Wall exchanges all disconnected. The engineers' first job was to lash the cables to prevent them falling into the street and then new lengths of cable had to be jointed in to restore service This operation took eleven pairs of jointers, working twelve hour shifts until 8pm on the 14th to complete the job. On 4th March, 1907[3], a fire at 11 - 12 Wood Street left the building entirely gutted by fire. The pole with a test box attached, which was mounted on the party wall, had to be replaced before cables and wires could be rejointed, taking two days to complete the job. The report concludes; 'A search party is looking for the test box.' There was a similar, though less serious, occurrence at 15B James Street, Haymarket, when a fire at Gaumont & Co., cinematograph specialists, destroyed five 52 pair cables and a cross connection box. Fortunately, although the premises were completely gutted by fire, the pole remained in position. The cables were drawn back to the adjoining buildings and the damaged portion renewed, so that service was restored by the following evening [4].

A rather unusual, if not unique, event took place on 28th February, 1905[5]. A fire was discovered at the Bank exchange premises in Queen Victoria Street and at the same time in the test room at Oxford Court, Cannon Street. The fire, in both cases, was caused by a live rail at Westminster Bridge station on the underground railway, being put in contact with the company's cable which ran through the tunnels, by a piece of metal troughing which had been carelessly left by the railway authorities. The result was that the test rooms in both exchanges were destroyed and over 2,000 exchange lines and 2,000 junctions left disconnected.

1 *The Electrician* 17th June, 1898
Heddon Street Fire: it appears that the top floor of the building which was burnt down, occupied by D Stuart, an electrical engineer, had formerly sheltered a telephone exchange and as a consequence over a hundred wires were supported by a derrick on the roof which fell in.
2 *NTJ* Oct 1906 p 147
3 *NTJ* May 1907 p 31
4 *NTJ* April 1907 p 16
5 *NTJ* Jan 1912 p 127

Junction box on the roof of a building in the City

THE EDWARDIAN TELEPHONE OPERATOR
WITH THE NATIONAL TELEPHONE COMPANY

Edwardian England saw a much needed change in the Victorian attitude towards working women. More young girls of middle class background found it necessary to add to the family income. The swift transition of the telephone from a curiosity to a commercial service came as a godsend to these women. It offered easy entry to white-collar work with no special training. Telephone work was regarded as a respectable employment, the main reason being that girls were protected from exposure to the public. They also had to be educated, well spoken and capable of answering customers un-ending requests. The National Telephone Company trainee operators started between 16 and 25 years old and were required to be 5ft 3ins without shoes. They were generally bright well educated intelligent girls, who are, in many cases, the daughters of professional men, doctors, barristers, clergymen and others.[1]

After passing a simple test in reading, writing and arithmetic followed by a medical, a girl started as a 'learner' in the company operating school earning 10/- [50p] a week. The first operating school for telephonists was opened at 58-59 London Wall in 1899 with thirty learners; Miss Ellen Ralph was placed in charge, assisted by two supervisors. Due to the fire at London Wall exchange in 1902 Miss Ralph and her staff were moved to a temporary school at the company's national headquarters at Telephone House on the Embankment[2]. This temporary school remained until September 1906, when it moved back to London Wall occupying a re-equipped suite of rooms. By this time the average number of learners had increased to seventy-five with a staff of ten supervisors. Ethel Epps was a supervisor at the school in 1903, where apparently 'she performed her duties with singular success in a position where peculiar qualities, apart from the essential detailed knowledge of the work, are needed in the training of the young telephonist[3]. Up to the end of May, 1907, some 3,000 pupils had passed through the school.

In two or three months the learner, 'as soon as she is efficient in her duties' graduated to a 'staff operator' to work alongside an experienced operator[4]. Her wages increased to a maximum of £1 a week after about five years, with ten days annual leave, increasing to fourteen days after two years.

Promotion to supervisor and then to Clerk-in-charge were open

London Wall operators' dining room, c.1900
The kitchens

Gerrard Exchange Kitchen

to the ambitious. An operator worked 42½ hours a week (day service was from 8 a m to 8 p m), with a 'late' and 'divided duty' bringing in extra money.

Forty-five minutes were allowed for dinner and fifteen minutes for tea, taken in the operators' dining room. Since 1897 the National Telephone Company had supplied exchanges with a kitchen and utensils, paying a woman to do the cooking. These Dinner Clubs were controlled by a committee elected by the girls themselves[5]. An operator could obtain a dinner at 5d and tea at ld and the menu was decided by the operators themselves. Few female operators worked after 8 p m and after 10 p m male operators took over until the following morning. Marriage automatically terminated a girl's employment, but she could become a reserve to be called upon in an emergency.

Few, if any, personal reflections of life as an Edwardian operator are available to us today, but in two contemporary accounts of an operator in London we read:
'with pardonable feminine vanity, the majority of young ladies wear gloves while operating to better protect, maintain the contour and complexion of their busy worked fingers and often conceals her ordinary walking habit under a loose kind of gown in dark material. This latter, was the kindly idea of the

National Telephone operator at turn of century, wearing an overall

National Telephone Company's administration, to shield a sensitive and modestly garbed operator from being distracted by an extra smart frock on either side of her[6].

'The telephone operator is healthy and the action of stretching her arms up above her head and to the right and left of her develops the chest and arms and turns thin and weedy girls after a few months work in the operating room into strong ones[7]. Prior to 1896 operators did not have the use of a headset, they had to speak into a

71

Operators being shown the location of telephone exchanges in the metropolitan area at the London Wall Training School

Miss Ralph taking a class at the London Wall School

mouth piece in the centre of a wooden box suspended in front of their faces on an adjustable apparatus. The receiver was held to the ear with one hand while the other manipulated the cords on the switchboard. Miss Amy Sims recalled that the first headgear receivers and breastplate transmitters were used at Oxford Court trunk exchange[8]. Ada Buckwell, who started as an operator at Westminster in June, 1896, remembered the introduction of 'headgear operating sets'. These were not regarded very favourably at first, but soon gained popularity with the operating staff[9]. Another problem to be overcome by the telephone companies in late Victorian times was the fashion for ladies to wear a bustle dress. Telephone operators found it hard to accommodate both themselves and a bustle on their chairs. So the back of the chairs were provided with an opening allowing the bustle to protrude. Many of these bustle hole chairs lasted long after the fashion changed and can be seen in photographs as late as 1910.

An operator who achieved the status of Supervisor and Clerk-in-Charge inherited a reputation as an awesome figure. She sat behind the girls where she could see them but they could not see her, and along with a team of higher ranking operators, monitored the performance of a girl, listening in to her telephone calls. A woman operator at a London exchange several decades ago recalled what her first supervisor was like:

'if she didn't choose to say "good morning" she didn't, she just sat there like the old Queen Mary when you went in, and we never called her by her christian name[10].

The National Telephone Company also provided a visiting matron who made tactful and sympathetic visits to the homes of sick operators. Should the illness be only minor then her certificate would be as acceptable as that of a doctor. She would keep the exchange managers informed about their absent staff and in many cases interest the parents of the girls in their work at the exchange. Due to her vigilance the National Telephone Company never had an epidemic of infectious illness at any of its London exchanges[11].

By the turn of the century the National Telephone Company had improved its working conditions considerably. Women were by now becoming more aware of their value in the work place. Fired by the suffrage movement that counted in their number National Telephone employees, like Katherine Pring. Miss Pring, after working as supervisor at London Wall and East, was promoted to Clerk-in-Charge at Sydenham. She was an active member, and was reported to have somewhat 'militant tendencies', having carried a banner from Trafalgar Square to Hyde Park[12]. That women were now prepared to stand up for their rights became only to clear to the National Telephone Company, with the case of the operators' strike at Holborn[13]. After the transfer of Holborn magneto exchange in St Andrews Street to the new C B no 1 at Birkbeck Chambers, the operators were told that on Tuesday, 21st June, 1904, they would be required to work a new rota. Their hours were to be increased from 8½ to 9, or 10, without any additional pay. This was discussed by the operators, and a petition was sent to the management demanding they return to their old rota working. They requested an answer in five days time. On arriving for work on the Saturday morning at 8 a m, a statement on the notice board implied that the matter was still receiving attention by the management. So 90 of the 99 girls in attendance refused to start work. The *Daily News* reported:

Something like a scene followed. The girls gathered in the numerous corridors and stairways of the building, almost choking the ingress and egress, discussing in subdued tones the position of affairs. In the exchange itself there was almost a panic. Instead of the night staff leaving at the usual hour, they were asked to continue and help was telephoned for from neighbouring exchanges. Several girls arrived from the Bank and Avenue offices, but, on learning the nature of the trouble, they at once sided with the strikers, and refused to start. Three girls who were sent from Kingston followed suit. In despair, a number of young ladies from the beginners' school were sent down, but as they were unfamiliar with the working of the switchboard they only made confusion worse confounded, and the effect was felt not only in the corridors of the exchange itself, but in the offices of the unfortunate subscribers whose business necessitated the use of the telephone during the hours when the trouble was at its highest.

As one girl told the *Reynolds* reporter "they have only got the few girls who would not came out, and a few of the supervisors, and the night staff of four men, have stayed on to assist." With the arrival of the Exchange Manager at 9.30 some of the girls went to see him and asked to return to the old 8½ hour rota. This was refused and so:

With a resource characteristic of the independent young lady of today, the leader of the strikers at once approached the agent who controls the letting of offices on the estate and asked for the use of an empty room where the position might be discussed. The request was at once granted, and on the

Reading subscribers' meters at Gerrard, c.1907
Trainee operators learning to use magneto and CB switchboards at London Wall Training School

third floor in a vacant office the girls appointed a committee to wait upon the Hon. Mrs Alfred Lyttleton with a view to soliciting her aid.

Help came from Mary McArthur of the Women's Trade Union League, who recorded in her diary for 25th June, that an 'emergency meeting of telephone operators on strike was held at the offices of the League.' In the meantime the exchange was being worked on an emergency footing;

A representative of *The Daily News*, that paper reported, seeking information from an official source at the exchange affected, was told with customary cheerfulness that 'there is nothing wrong'. As a proof of this statement the journalist was invited up into the switchroom to see for himself that all the boards were occupied, and that the business was progressing as usual. The boards certainly contained their full complement of operators; that business was 'progressing' as usual was not, however, so clear. A certain air of strangeness about the majority suggested the inquiry whether this was the usual staff. It was at once admitted that a number of operators were new hands from other exchanges, although just how many they were, the informant, although the manager, did not know.

Eventually the dispute was settled by a deputation of operators meeting the General Manager, Mr

Gaine. He pointed out that no duty had been imposed on them in excess of their contract, but he thought some of the hours of duty were unduly long. He gave instructions for the timetable to be altered back to an 8½ hour day during the week, and 6 hours on Saturday, with an hour for tea and dinner. The operators were jubilant and streams of young ladies flooded Birkbeck Buildings, converging on Room 326, which was soon crowded to suffocation. Within a month the National Association of Telephone Operators was founded to look after their future interests.

The working conditions of the Edwardian operator was also dictated by influences outside her control. Here we have a log of events that took place at Paddington exchange, during the summer of 1911[14].

SERVICE DIFFICULTIES IN A LONDON EXCHANGE.

By G Buckeridge,
Exchange Manager, Paddington.

Following on a full season, with extra traffic induced by the Coronation festivities, we have been subjected during July and August, usually slack months, to the effects produced by abnormal heat, heavy storms and labour disputes, which have all caused the telephone to be largely used as a means of communication. During the heat the telephone has undoubtedly been a great saver of physical energy from the public point of view, but it has been very trying for the operating staff, who, depleted by the holidays and debilitated by the heat themselves, have been called upon again and again for special effort, when, as a rule, they are enabled to take things more easily.

As if the heat were not enough, 28th July was the occasion of the most disastrous rain and thunderstorm we have experienced, from the telephone point of view, for several years in London. As a result of the storm there were over 200 lines affected on Paddington, 175

actually being out of order. These lines were of course, put 'O.K.' in a few days, but the faults had a marked effect on the quality of the service, and in addition, necessitated the provision of one additional testing operator, 200 plugged up circuits and ten extra transfer circuits to the testing position, so that enquiries for lines out of order could be dealt with.

While the storm was in progress it was found that the lantern light window sashes had shrunk owing

Edwardian operators' rest room at London Wall. The National Telephone Company furnished all rest rooms in a similar fashion

to the long drought previously and allowed the rain, tropical in its volume and intensity, to rush in to such an extent that the staff was flooded out in a few seconds. As a consequence for a quarter of an hour the major portion of the 'A' operators had to leave their positions and it was not until sheets were obtained and the switchboard and operators protected that work could be resumed. It was found then that the water had percolated through the key shelves into the aprons in many cases, though not in sufficient quantity to do more than soak a few cords.

The interruptions, taking into consideration the number of circuits affected, were not serious here, but for a few days complaints were general both of intermittent faults and of difficulty in getting numbers owing to their being out of order.

Hardly had the effect of the storm interruption been overcome than the traffic was affected by labour disputes. This was marked by the number of complaints it excited through the difficulty in obtaining communication with the railways and large carriers. Personally I dealt with several cases where the callers had waited some

hours for Carter Paterson and the G.E. and G.W. goods departments. In each case it was impossible to help in any way, the unfortunate callers eventually having to take their chance of a connection. They appeared reconciled to the situation, though whether this frame of mind will continue in the event of further strike development remains to be seen.

Already it has been necessary here in two cases to reserve lines for outgoing calls from railways where they have groups of lines, as they complain that incoming connections were put through so quickly as to make it impossible for them to get messages out at all.

1 *Every Woman's Encyclopedia* date unknown circa -1910-14.
NTJ Dec, 1906 p 193.
2 *NTJ* July, 1907 p 75.
3 *NTJ* Jan, 1910 p 207
4 *Every Woman's Encyclopedia*.
5 *NTJ* March, 1911 p 258.
6 *Living London* Sims 1902.
7 *Every Woman's Encyclopaedia*.
8 *NTJ* Nov, 1908 p 159.
9 *NTJ* July, 1911 p 72.
10 Brenda Maddox *Telecommunication Journal* Dec, 1975 p 711
11 *NTJ* March 1911 p 258
12 *NTJ* May, 1909 p 29
13 Details from the *Post Office Engineering Union Journal*, 1962.
14 *NTJ* Sept, 1911 p 129

THE NATIONAL TELEPHONE COMPANY'S ENGINEERS AND ELECTRICIANS

The Metropolitan Electrician, and his assistant, was responsible for the maintenance and provision of all telephone equipment in the London area. In charge of the exchange and subscribers' equipment was the Metropolitan Maintenance Electrician. The Metropolitan Engineer supervised work on external overhead wires and cables.

The Exchange Electrician was directly responsible for the condition of all the exchange and subscribers' apparatus within his area. He supervised all the maintenance staff and acted as mediator for the company with subscribers suffering from exceptional troubles and he had to see that monthly estimates of expenditure were adhered to. Under the Exchange Electrician's control were the Exchange and Subscriber's Instrument Inspectors, the Test Clerks and Fault Finders. The policy of the company was to give every member of the technical staff as much knowledge as possible to perform their duty efficiently.

The provision of the subscribers' instruments came under the control of the Divisional Fitter. He arranged for the Fitter to carry out installation work in the area that was then inspected by the Fitting Inspector. The company staff concentrated on installing subscribers' instruments and both large and small private exchanges in large office blocks, department stores and hotels, while the replacement of the old magneto exchanges with new C.B. No I equipment was carried out by outside contractors. These changeovers caused quite an amount of ill feeling with subscribers who objected to the new telephone instruments supplied and an extreme amount of patience and tactful persuasion was necessary to have the new telephones accepted. Sudden affection was shown for the old instrument that had up until then been a source of complaint, many reasons being put forward to the change. The main objection was to the loss of the hand micro-telephone with its speak key, and subscribers prone to impatience did not like losing their hand generator with which 'to grind the machine' providing relief to their feelings. Some did not want fixed transmitters, while others made a strong point of the new instruments non-adaptability to height. Even after conversion numbers of subscribers wanted the old instruments back, one city gent went so far as to offer £50 for the return of his hand micro-telephone set.

Life as an employee of the National Telephone Company's engineering and electrical staff was tough, Mr Weinel remembered

Fitting office at Gerrard, May, 1910

being demobbed from the army at the end of the Boer War and signing on for the National Telephone Company at their Kensington exchange as a labourer at 22 shillings for a 54 hour week[1]. There were no holidays except Bank Holidays and below the rank of Foreman there was no sick pay, although where necessary a lodging allowance of 6d a night was payable. Sacking labourers was quite common, though there was competition between the exchange managers for skilled men's services. The work of the internal staff was with relatively simple telephone sets and exchange wiring.

Ted Skyring remembered joining the National Telephone Company at London Wall in 1899 as an Instrument Inspector earning 22/6d. a week[2]. Each Instrument Inspector was given a district within which he was responsible for the maintenance of subscribers' lines. His district was in the City of London around Cheapside. He recalls 'one either got on or got the sack.' Mr Weinel reflects that in the main both the internal and external staff were a hard working and hard drinking crowd, working always in the shadow of unemployment or suspension or stoppage of a day's pay at the whim of any of the higher officers for even such small things as breaking one slate on a roof.

The general public's inability to comprehend the more technical aspects of the telephone, provided both the maintenance and constructional departments with a number of amusing anecdotes. When the Instrument Inspector enquired as to which receiver was broken the subscriber replied, "Well, it's not the receiver you listen with, but the one that you put to your ear to stop the noise coming through!" This, of course, shows some familiarity with the speaking tube. Another instance along these lines was recalled by a fitter, who, after providing a private circuit between two switchboards, one of which had just been moved into new premises, tried the line from the distant end. Unable to obtain any response, he returned, to be greeted by a builders' man

Test and fault clerks checking subscribers' lines at Gerrard, 1910

with. "Was that you ringing? I thought it was you, and shouted down the hole you had been working on, but couldn't hear anything, so gave it up." He had been spending his energy shouting in to the jack. A second fitter tracing some old wiring to a water pipe (earth return) was remarked to by the subscriber, "Oh! the old tenant evidently had a telephone to the water company." At a naturalist's in East London an inspector was startled to find at the end of an examination of the instrument protector that all his operations had been carefully watched by a large chimpanzee. Two hours later the man, on passing the premises, was dragged in by the proprietor, and told that the telephone was out of order. It was found that the monkey had taken the protector cover off, removed the fuses and heat coils and deposited the treasure trove in his bed of straw. A curious fault was found on a line that was an aged survivor of earth circuit times. It was reported for intermittently refusing to work. After much tribulation it was discovered that when the tide was low the earth plate which was sunk in the river bed got quite dry, hence the stoppage.

1 The Post Office Engineering Union,
2 *The History of the Post Office Engineers Union 1870-1970*. Frank Bealey.

The switchboard in the Oxford Court Trunk Exchange in 1889. Note the Blake transmitters hanging in front of the operators' positions with watch receiver hanging behind or 'engaged' testing.

THE ELECTROPHONE STORY

The rapidly developing London telephone system was by no means only used for the spoken word. Another use was found in utilising the telephone network to distribute entertainment into the home, and was first explored commercially in the late 1800s. In Paris a system called Theatrephone was developed by which live entertainment was wired, via a switchboard, to any who wished to subscribe.

In London a syndicate was formed by Mr M S J Booth in 1893 to work certain patents for the telephone transmission of theatrical and other performances, over the system of the National Telephone Company. By 1894 the syndicate became known as Electrophone Ltd. Confined at first to the Metropolitan area of London, the service:

'enables telephone subscribers to listen to performances at selected theatres, music halls and concert halls, while sitting at their ease in their homes, connections are also made to some of the City and West End churches[1].

The main distribution centre for the operation was eventually installed in the old Pelican Club which was taken over in 1895 by

The Electrophone Listening Room in the old Gerrard Exchange, with the inglenook that was part of the Pelican Club

83

the National Telephone Company for their new Gerrard Exchange. It consisted of a switchboard with specially wired cord circuits. On the multiple jacks were terminated incoming junctions from various exchanges along with the incoming lines from theatres, etc.

To become connected to the Electrophone service it was necessary for the subscriber to ask the local exchange for Electrophone service. Interconnection was made to the local Electrophone position and from there, via a specially designated junction, to the Electrophone exchange in Gerrard Street. Here the subscriber was cross connected with the required theatre, etc.. By the end of the first year there were some forty-seven subscribers to the system.

For those who wished, an Electrophone Saloon was provided in Gerrard exchange, where performances could be listened to; this was available to those who did not regularly subscribe to the service. In this saloon was a wonderful ingle-nook fireplace that was part of the original Pelican Club[2]. A trade card of the period advertises the saloon, as:
'Quaintly decorated by Messrs Hooydonk Ltd., Old Burlington Street. To sit in ones armchair and listen to the favourite items of entertainment in progress at the leading London theatres and music halls is certainly an agreeable

method of spending an hour or two.'

By the turn of the century the Gerrard Magneto Manual Exchange in the old Pelican Club premises was not large enough to cope with the growth of the telephone demand in the West End area, so the National Telephone Company bought up two houses adjoining the exchange and constructed a new

Party seated round an Electrophone table in the new saloon at 36 Gerrard Street

building. In September, 1907, the changeover took place and in the half completed building next door the new CB exchange came into use.

Before demolition of the old building could take place the Electrophone board had to be moved, so a lease was taken out on 36 Gerrard Street (this building still stands today) and the Electrophone exchange was moved in, and a new listening saloon was also constructed.

Electrophone subscribers had increased to around 600 by 1908 and covered performances and services from some 30 theatres and churches.

By the time the National Telephone Company was transferred to the Post Office in 1912, it was a most flourishing concern. During the First World War

The Gerrard Electrophone Exchange in the old Pelican Club building, c.1900

considerable development took place and growth was so rapid that before long the old exchange was quite outgrown and it became necessary to provide a new one. The extent of the system can be gauged by entries in an old Exchange Construction Estimate Book of 1919-1920 where references are made to work being carried out for Electrophone facilities at exchanges as far from Gerrard as Willesden, Park, Ealing and Chiswick.

In June, 1919, the design for the new Electrophone exchange was prepared by the staff of the London Engineering District and in due course a new suite of boards was constructed by the District staff and opened in March, 1920. The new boards consisted of alternate music positions and switching transfer positions. The switching and transfer positions were arranged so that the maximum load for an operator was 50 connections. The operator of the music positions was responsible for switching on the batteries at the theatre or music hall, etc. when that circuit was required.

The transmitters in the theatre were mounted on heavy bases

suspended by rubber bands and were arranged according to the instructions issued in 1896:
'the transmitters should not be fitted in close proximity to the bass drum or the trombone of the orchestra[3].'

The reason for this caution was that the Blake and Alder transmitters used in the early days of Electrophone tended to jar and vibrate unpleasantly when subjected to loud passages of music. This was eventually overcome by the introduction of a form of granular carbon transmitter.

The traffic at the Electrophone Exchange was peculiar in as much as the operators had a large number of connections to be made at the commencement of each period of service and little to do after. The charge for the service in the 1920's was advertised as £10 for four persons and £5 for two; under 2d a day. The £10 rental provided the subscriber with four receiver sets and a hand transmitter along with an attractive tripod table on which the receiving sets could be stored when not in use For £5 the subscriber only got two receivers, no transmitter or table. The advantages of the table installation was that the subscriber could signal the Electrophone board without having to leave the room to use the telephone as was necessary when on the cheaper rental.

The arrangements for working after the Post Office take-over in 1912 were; the Postmaster General, provided, installed and maintained all the apparatus and lines, whilst the company undertook to operate the Electrophone exchange. A look through the Electrophone file at the Post Office archives reveals a constant correspondence battle between Mr Booth and the Postmasters General as to the quality of the service given. The company often accused the Post Office of complacency in providing plant and argued that the Post Office should promote the company. Gradually the number of subscribers declined and, in 1925, the Post Office took over the company and brought about its eventual liquidation. The recovery of the Electrophone plant at Gerrard, Mayfair, Museum, Victoria, Holborn, Langham and Grosvenor exchanges was estimated at £3,301 and approval for the work was given in October of that year, hastened on by the advent of moving pictures with sound and the embryo of the BBC wireless system.

1 *The Telegraph and Telephone Journal* May, 1920 p 125.
2 The removal date of the saloon to 36 Gerrard Street is unclear, but the room was also used as an operators' dining room at one stage.
3 *The Story of the Telephone* J M Robertson p 86.

'GERRARD ONE'
THE STORY OF A PRESTIGE
TELEPHONE NUMBER

The West End of Edwardian times was already a thriving shopping district, where many of today's department stores were already established and had telephone connections, Dickins & Jones, Gerrard 3640; Debenham & Freebody, Gerrard 3549; and Liberty's, Gerrard 3658; along with two that have now disappeared, Swan & Edgar, Gerrard 3586; and Marshall & Snelgrove 334-348 Oxford St, Gerrard 3561. They were all listed in the United Telephone Company directory of 1884-5.

Perhaps the most flamboyant store of this period opened in March, 1909, and was named after its owner, Gordon Selfridge. Selfridge's telephone number was Gerrard 1, and was obtained purely by accident. Mr Selfridge later explained that he had asked the National Telephone Company to allow him to install a public exchange in his store, but that in declining the suggestion, they had, 'most apologetically' offered him this number. He recognised that this number was worth a thousand pounds spot cash for publicity alone, so while appearing only nonchalantly interested, he made

sure that he accepted the offer, that was to cause such speculation and comment at the time.

Mr A C Greening of Gerrard exchange wrote -
'A bold innovation was instituted by the firm when they allotted a position for their switchboard right out in the open store, in the very centre of the handsome building just completed. A rail serves to separate the operators from the public, and the novel sight of a telephone switchboard operated in the open, attracted at all times a crowd of onlookers standing six to eight deep throughout each day of the inaugural week. So great was the pressure on the opening day that the rail and its supports were thrown down, and it became necessary to build a barricade of heavy carpet rolls standing on end, round the switchboard, thereby permitting an adequate view while preserving the necessary facilities for handling calls. Many onlookers were noted as having stood through periods varying from 30 minutes to 1 hour, altogether fascinated by telephone operating, any comments they felt impelled to make being made in subdued whispers. This unique method of bringing the public face to face with a little known section of their work provided considerable interest in the members of the National Telephone Company staff present.'

Selfridge's opened with a three position switchboard with 130 extensions. These were mostly fitted with coin collecting boxes in fact the restaurant had fifty-four jacks installed for these pay station telephones. The board by 1914 had grown to six positions of 40 lines and 184 extensions and by 1915 to nine positions, 10 lines and 265 extensions, showing how shopping by telephone had grown in popularity. In 1915 Selfridge's introduced a new feature which they widely advertised:

'Ladies wishing to give orders which refer to a number of departments are provided with comfortable chairs and tables and the services of assistants and at their elbow is placed a pedestal telephone. The assistants take particulars of the articles required, samples are brought in immediately for inspection and if madam desires to consult her housekeeper or cook on any question of domestic economy which she may be dealing with, the telephone enables her to make free calls for this purpose.'

1 *NTJ* April 1909 p 7
Also *The Telegraph and Telephone Journal* April, 1911 p 154

Constructing the flat self-restoring indicator branching multiple switchboard at Gerrard Exchange, 1895

CONCLUSION

In February, 1905, the government purchased the National Telephone Company when its licence expired at the end of 1911. Under the agreement the Postmaster General had the right to object to purchasing any of the company's exchanges and equipment that was considered unsuitable, in areas where the two organisations were in competition. By the end of 1910 notices were served on a number of National Telephone Company exchanges in London. The reason given was that the equipment was not wanted by the Post Office because it intended to erect duplicate exchanges of its own.

Avenue was one of the exchanges objected to as it was still working on the old self restoring indicator branching multiple, fitted in August, 1894, and largely served by overhead cables and wires. As this was considered unsuitable for the future, the Post Office constructed a new Avenue exchange with a C B No 1 switchboard. This was planned to open on the first of January, 1912, when the company's system was transferred into Post Office control, thereby replacing the old National Telephone Company exchange, which was then scrapped.

At Bank exchange the amount of purchase money asked for by the National Telephone Company could not be agreed to by the Post Office, which considered the exchange equipment to be obsolete. Not long before the transfer of the National Telephone Company was due to take place, the Post Office realised that many influential subscribers in the city were on Bank exchange and would have no service. The National Telephone Company was approached for the Bank exchange record cards, but were informed that the records were part of the exchange that the Post Office was not buying. The matter was hurriedly re-opened and the purchase of Bank was finally agreed. Bank exchange survived another 14 years, eventually closing on 5th June, 1926, when the old horizontal switchboard was finally scrapped.

Westminster was closed in 1911, being absorbed by the Post Office exchange at Victoria. All the other National Telephone Company exchanges were transferred into Post Office control from 1st January, 1912.

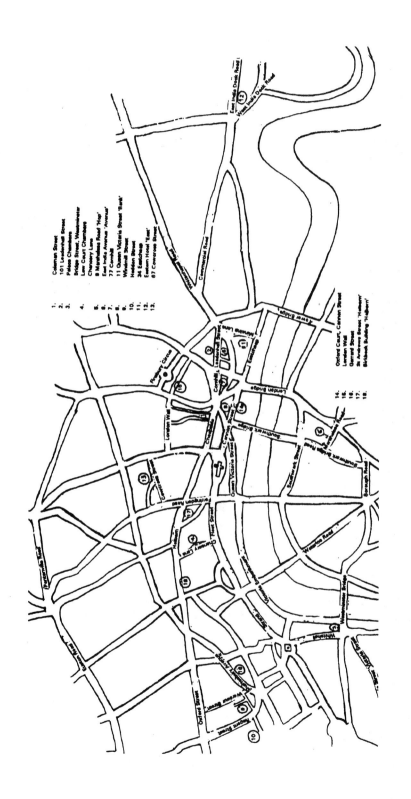

1. Coleman Street
2. 101 Leadenhall Street
3. Palace Chambers
4. Bridge Street, Westminster
5. Lew Court Chambers
   Chancery Lane
6. 8 Marchalsea Road 'Mar'
7. East India Avenue 'Avenue'
8. 77 Cornhill
9. 11 Queen Victoria Street 'Bank'
10. Heddon Street
11. Windmill Street
12. 34 Eastcheap
13. Eastern Hotel 'East'
    67 Cavarnes Street

14. Oxford Court, Cannon Street
15. London Wall
16. Garrard Street
17. St Andrews Street 'Holborn'
18. Birkbeck Building 'Holborn'